The

Jacksons of Tennessee

Also by Marguerite Vance

LADY JANE GREY, RELUCTANT QUEEN

MARIE ANTOINETTE, DAUGHTER OF AN EMPRESS

THE LEES OF ARLINGTON

PATSY JEFFERSON OF MONTICELLO

MARTHA, DAUGHTER OF VIRGINIA

WHILE SHEPHERDS WATCHED

CAPITALS OF THE WORLD

PAULA

PAULA GOES AWAY TO SCHOOL

MARTA

A STAR FOR HANSI

E·P·DUTTON & CO.INC

1852 1953

CREATIVE · IOI YEARS · PUBLISHING

The
Jacksons of Tennessee

By
MARGUERITE VANCE

Illustrated by
NEDDA WALKER

NEW YORK
E. P. DUTTON & COMPANY, INC.
1953

LIBRARY OF CONGRESS CATALOG CARD NUMBER: 53-6082

53- 18824

For

MONICA *and* GWYNNE MACRAE

VANCE   THE JACKSONS OF TENNESSEE
Rachel and Andrew Jackson, strong of
spirit, and united in their deep love
for their country, achieved a happy
marriage at Hunter's Hill and The
Hermitage.

CONTENTS

		PAGE
Chapter 1	PIONEERS WESTWARD	15
Chapter 2	A MEETING	33
Chapter 3	HARRODSBURG	47
Chapter 4	THE DONELSON STATION	71
Chapter 5	FUTILE JOURNEY	83
Chapter 6	FLIGHT	95
Chapter 7	NATCHEZ	107
Chapter 8	HUNTER'S HILL	121
Chapter 9	THE HERMITAGE	133
Chapter 10	THE PASSING YEARS	147
Chapter 11	TOGETHER	161

ACKNOWLEDGEMENT

ACKNOWLEDGEMENT is made to the following for help in preparing the manuscript:

BEGINNINGS OF WEST TENNESSEE, In the Land of the Chickasaws, By Samuel Cole Williams—Watauga Press, 1930

THE LIFE OF ANDREW JACKSON, By Marquis James—Garden City Publishing Company, 1938

HOME AT THE HERMITAGE, By Alfred Leland Crabb—Bobbs-Merril Company, 1948

SOME AMERICAN LADIES, By Meade Minnegrode—G.P. Putnam's Sons, 1926

THE PRESIDENT'S LADY, By Irving Stone—Doubleday and Company, 1951

THE CAVALIER OF TENNESSEE, By Meredith Nicholson—Bobbs-Merril Company, 1928

EPIC OF AMERICA, By James Truslow Adams—Little, Brown and Company, 1933

AGE OF JACKSON, By Arthur M. Schlesinger—Little, Brown and Company, 1945

FIRST FIRST LADIES, By Mary Ormsbee Whitton—Hastings House, 1948

RACHEL JACKSON, By Nellie Treanor Stokes—Ladies' Hermitage Association, 1942

THE HERMITAGE, (Originally compiled by Mrs. Mary C. Dorris. Revised June, 1951)— Ladies' Hermitage Association

GENERAL JACKSON'S LADY, By Mary French Caldwell—Published by the author with the cooperation of the Ladies' Hermitage Association, 1936

ANDREW JACKSON, By Genevieve Foster—Charles Scribner's Sons, 1951

THE WILDERNESS ROAD, By Robert L. Kincaid—Bobbs-Merril Company, 1947

NATCHEZ ON THE MISSISSIPPI, By Harnet T. Kane—William Morrow and Company, 1947

DEEP DELTA COUNTRY, By Harnet T. Kane—Duell, Sloan and Pearce, Inc., 1944

SHORT HISTORY OF THE UNITED STATES, By John Spencer Bassett—The Macmillan Company, 1929

AUTHOR'S NOTE

IN PRESENTING this work to the reader is occurs to me that something should be said of the very nature of the story. It is the story of a woman—it is much more Rachel's story than her husband's—who refused to let the beauty and dignity of her marriage be marred by ugly rumor and unjustified criticism.

It is impossible to write a story of Rachel Jackson's life without making the tragedy which marred so much of it an integral part of that story. To have omitted her early marriage to Lewis Robards, the spurious divorce, her marriage to Andrew Jackson and the subsequent scandal when it was learned they had lived as man and wife for two years in the innocent belief that her divorce from Robards had been granted—this would have meant not writing the story at all. Not a single source of reference failed to confirm this. For that was—and is—her story. In the end it was the indirect cause of her death. But meanwhile the years between had been filled and brimming over with the joy, the never ending kindness that Rachel Jackson took with her wherever she went.

Girls today are realists; they do not require truths masked in sugary disguises. So I have given them Rachel Jackson from the time she was a happy girl in Virginia until her death as the adored wife of Andrew Jackson who said of her:

> "I can forgive all who have wronged me but I will have to pray fervently that I may have the grace to enable me to forget or forgive any enemy who has ever maligned that blessed one . . . ."

June 13, 1953   MARGUERITE VANCE

The
Jacksons of Tennessee

Chapter 1

PIONEERS WESTWARD

APRIL sunshine set the waters of the Cumberland sparkling like a diamond-spattered length of undulating green
ribbon. A cool wind set the wash on a line strung across the
flatboat's width dancing wildly, heel and toe, heel and toe.
It penetrated even the warmest homespun. A sudden gust
whipped black curls from under a young girl's bonnet and
sent her scurrying to take shelter behind a pile of household goods stacked amidships. She laughed as she tucked
in the curls, wrapped her cape more tightly about her and,
snug in her sheltered nook, continued to watch the forest
sliding by.

The delicate yellow-green screen of new leaves was broken here and there by a bold slashing of redbud and dogwood. Wild syringa waved its clusters of white stars against the screen's lacy pattern; birds, their feathers ruffled, were blown before the gale, whistling shrilly.

Laughter died on the girl's lips and her eyes grew somber. In less than an hour from now they would be home—brother Alexander had said so. Home? She turned for a better view of the tall, rather bleak-visaged man handling the sweep in the stern of the boat. Alexander — William — Johnny — Stockley — they'd all come safely back from the war, all so much older, somehow so very much wiser. Severn hadn't been strong enough to go and Samuel they said was too young. For this she had been thankful for Samuel was her favorite brother. Leven was the baby, two years younger than she — and Rachel Donelson was twelve and a half. Her sisters May and Catherine were married and had growing families. That left only Jane, fifteen, to be her real companion.

"Ra-a-a-ch-el, Oh, Ra-a-a-ch-el?" It was Catherine's five-year-old son calling. Little Johnny Hutchings was a croupy child who had kept his mother in a constant state of nerves during the voyage. Now his voice rose sharply from the prow and in another moment he came plodding around the corner of his young aunt's cozy shelter. He was bundled in a heavy coat, a cap drawn down on his head, and out of his wrappings his small unhappy face peered like that of an angry gnome.

"Rachel," he was very close to tears, "Mama says mayhap

we'll sleep in tents again tonight and — Luke says th' Indians are just waiting for us to go to sleep and then —then — he says they'll give a big war whoop and scalp us all—he said so, Luke did!"

Rachel frowned and put an arm around the small bundle of misery and drew it to her in pity. Why must there always be a bully who loved to torment younger children? Johnny's pinched little nose was so red, such abject desolation was spread across his face. Before Rachel could answer him, he drew a deep breath and continued. "And," he drew forth his left hand from his right sleeve where he had been hugging it to him, "and my chap hurts. Mama said you had th' goose grease and . . . . "

The small gnome looked up at her with eyes watering in the cold wind and sniffed. Rachel got out her handkerchief. "Blow, lamb," she commanded, and when he had obeyed with a vigor that almost jarred him off his feet, she drew him farther in out of the gale. "Now, now, Johnny," she comforted, crouching on her heels before him, "don't let Luke tease you. You know he loves to talk biggety just to scare you children. Maybe there will be Indians, but they're not going to scalp us. Let me see your hand. . . ."

Her own hands were rough from constant washing in icy water but her fingers were wonderfully gentle as she turned the little boy's delicate wrist on her palm. The skin of the hand was cracked and tiny flecks of blood dotted the knuckles.

"La, Johnny, I should think the chap *would* hurt," she

said. "But where are your mittens?" Asked of any other little
boy, the question would have been silly. What boy wears
mittens in April? But with Johnny Hutchings it was different, and even as she asked, she was reaching into her
skirt pocket for the little jar she knew she would find there.
Since December Rachel Donelson had kept an eye on all the
small chapped hands aboard the *Adventure*.

"Here—hold still." Deftly she daubed the balsam-scented
goose fat on the smarting knuckles, ran an expert hand over
the coat pockets and brought out the forgotten mittens.
"Now put these on and run and tell Mattie to come and
take down the wash. I reckon she forgot. Alexander says
we'll be stopping pretty soon."

She gave him a reassuring pat and he trotted off. In a few
minutes she followed him, for the *Adventure* was slowing
and her father was shouting orders to the boat just behind
whose pilot in turn relayed the command down the line. The
entire flotilla slowed. Now a cabin came into view along the
shore—another and another, now a cluster of tents. Men
were running down to the water's edge, shouting greetings
and were hailed by passengers aboard the flatboats. The
voyage was over at last. One hundred and twenty women
and children under the protection of forty intrepid frontiersmen had traveled almost a thousand miles of waterways and
finally had reached their goal, the Big Bend of the Cumberland at a spot known as the Great Salt Lick, or the French
Lick, not far from the Nashville of today.

In her sturdy watertight boots Rachel squelched ashore,

over the slippery mud, through the delicately curling young ferns, up to the door of the cabin her father pointed out. In spite of the sunshine, the wind continued cold and she joined her shivering laugh of appreciation to her mother's as they made way for Hector, the servant, who came striding after them with an enormous armload of firewood. Just to be *inside* once more and inside something that did not sway and groan and resound to many voices, that in itself was cause enough for happy laughter. Here, in this snug cabin, Rachel, Jane, Leven and their parents would live for the time being. Married brothers and sisters would share their cabins with bachelor brothers; or the bachelors might prefer tents for their temporary homes.

How that first day passed Rachel never could recall. Her father was everywhere, cheering, encouraging the settlers; there was much laughter and running from cabin to cabin, children racing, shouting, frantic with pent up vigor and a renewed sense of security. They were no longer traveling toward the unknown; they were home. Women rummaged in boxes for favorite cooking pots, neighbor calling to neighbor in an excess of good feeling, bending over kettles on new hearths, testing new cranes and pothooks. Meals were eaten, evening came, and before it was quite dark most cabins, the Donelsons' among them, were still for the night.

However, once on the feather tick which she was to share with Jane, Rachel found she could not sleep. Over-stimulated, over-tired and now suddenly missing the noisy boat, she twisted and turned, staring into the dark. The forest was so still. Far away a cougar proclaimed its loneliness; crickets chirrred. Otherwise no sound broke the silence.

Rachel tossed, thinking in spite of herself of what Luke had said to Johnny. Indians . . . suppose they did come! What could Papa, what could all the men in the settlement do against a determined war party? But this wouldn't do, she told herself sternly. Better think about something else, think of the stories Mama used to tell her and Janie about her own girlhood on Virginia's Eastern Shore.

At seventeen Rachel Stockley had been a beautiful girl, full of the winsome airs and grace of a belle from the Eastern Shore. Her father's lands had spread out across Accomac County in the rich Virginia Colony, and suitors with imposing family names came on horseback and by coach to pay court to the girl whose beauty and rich dowry made her a rare prize. But it was John Donelson who had won her, John Donelson from the western part of the state, a man of high honor and integrity, twenty-six, established in business. Young Donelson owned a small iron foundry on the Pigg River and rich land holdings on the Bannister in Pittsylvania County.

So Rachel Stockley had taken her fine linens and silver and burnished mahogany, her slaves and her saddle horses, and had followed her young husband into a new life.

This must have been in the early 1740's when in another Virginia county little Martha Dandridge, one day to be Martha Washington, was learning to ride her pony, Dancer, along the banks of the Pamunkey River.

Rachel Donelson found life in the western part of the state a little more rugged, a little less luxurious than the easy way of life she had known. As mistress of her husband's plantation she was responsible for the health and bodily welfare of his slaves as well as those she brought with her. There was spinning and weaving to be taught the women, clothing to be made, a substantial plantation house to be kept in shining order. And presently there was a baby son to care for.

With the passing years John Donelson's iron works prospered, his land increased and his position in the state took on importance and stature. In 1769 he was chosen representative of his county in the House of Burgesses under the Royal Governor, Lord Boutetourt. Other members of the House at the time were George Washington, Thomas Jefferson and Patrick Henry.

England, the mother country, was becoming increasingly interested in the western wilderness, held for the most part by the Indians. Lord Boutetourt, though he recognized John Donelson as one of the more liberty loving Virginians, still had the utmost confidence in him both as a leader and as a man to be trusted in his negotiations with the Indians. So it was that Donelson was chosen, with John Stuart, to negotiate with the Cherokees for purchase of some of their western land. Later it was Donelson who was sent into the Indian country to run lines of demarkation which would show just which lands were being sold to the white men and which were to remain in Indian hands.

He was almost middle-aged now, a man of means whose

fine sense of honorable dealing made him perfect in any situation requiring diplomacy and clear, unhampered thinking. So in the spring of 1771 Colonel John Donelson set out with his maps and his surveyor's instruments.

Back in the comfortable plantation house on the Bannister he had left a large, happy, though anxious family. Leven was a two-year-old toddler, Rachel, four, a black-haired, mischievous romp with a will of her own and melting dark eyes to wreck any possible opposition to that will. Of all the children she probably missed her father most. She was his pet, his baby girl who ran to meet him, arms out-flung, when he returned from his frequent trips to Williamsburg. Round-eyed, she curled in his lap before the fire, blissfully content while she listened to his stories of the Governor's palace, his coach-and-six, his liveried outriders.

Now Papa was away, his absence a matter of months, and his return only a pause before he must be off again on the Colony's business in the West. Meanwhile, war with England took the older boys away from home, and the family circle for several years was often sadly shrunken.

Rachel was always to remember how, from the day of his first return from the West, her father's whole attitude toward the home plantation had changed. Perhaps the little girl realized it only subconsciously, possibly the knowledge came slowly without a full realization of its meaning, at least not just at first.

Alexander, William, John, Catherine's husband Tom Hutchings, all the men folk gathered around the supper table, talked more and more of one thing: the Cumberland. Rachel could not be sure whether the Big Salt Lick, the French Lick, the Big Bend, Fort Nashborough and the Cumberland all meant the same thing, but as time passed and the names became increasingly familiar, she felt sure they must. She was nine, then ten and eleven years old while the war, like an ugly blot, sprawled across the land. Then Colonel Donelson came home, either from service with the army or from one of his journeys into the wilderness, and immediately began making plans to move his family west.

(On her feather tick, Rachel drew the heavy blanket closer, remembering the changes that had followed so closely.) The iron works from which came her treasured tiny cooking utensils, was sold. Next, strangers came to ride over the plantation, asking questions, peering into the kitchen and weaving room. And all the time Mama and the older girls and the house servants who could spin and weave and sew, were working feverishly making clothes and bedding. Preserving too, came in for extra flourishes until every hogshed, crock and firkin was filled, and the smoke house bulged with its store of smoked hams and bacon.

Jane one day tossed her pretty head. "But why, I ask you, must we leave here and go West with a lot of people we don't know—and Indians and everything!"

Her sister Mary, rocking her youngest baby, smiled at her over the little bobbing head. "Stop being uppity, Janie," she said. "Virginia's only a mighty small part of America, after all, you know. There're more hundreds of miles of rich

land west of us than you can even imagine. Papa saw it all—
at least much of it— and he thinks there will be more there
for us, that is in years to come, than there could possibly
be here."

The baby became fretful and Rachel put down her knitting and took him, holding him against her shoulder as she
walked up and down the room. "Besides, Janie," she added,
"think of the fun of being on a boat, a flatboat, and going up
the rivers Papa says we will! And as for the people we don't
know—sh, sh, sh,—well, they don't know us, either. Maybe
they don't like the idea of being with you any more than you
do being with them—hush, honey baby,—and I think for my
part it'll be fun. Wait and see!"

Jane sniffed. "I will," she said and sailed out of the room
lest her sisters see that her chin was quivering.

So the summer had passed and with the October days and
the gathering of the harvest, the Donelson clan made ready
to leave. Their immediate destination would be the great
pioneer meeting place, the Block House on the Holston
River. Here would gather the families that were making
the trek into the wilderness. Here some of the men would
leave their wives and children in Colonel Donelson's care
and would take the more hazardous overland route. Colonel
Donelson, with Captain Richard Henderson, second in command, would undertake to pilot the fleet of flatboats down
the Holston River to the Tennessee, on to the Ohio and
finally the Cumberland, until they reached the Great Salt
Lick near Fort Nashborough. The men taking the overland

route would be led by Colonel James Robertson, one of the ablest leaders of the western migration.

Rachel had loved the tangy autumn days of waiting at the Block House as more and more families arrived. There were the Robertsons, the Cartwrights, the Peytons, the Blackmores, the Harrisons and many more. There were boys and girls her own age as eager as she to be off on the great adventure. Excitement was in the air; wives and sweethearts bravely said good-by to men who were going overland; boys not yet men but longing to be, exasperated their mothers by venturing beyond bounds into the forest, then returning with chilling tales of having seen a mammoth bear, of having escaped a wild cat by sheer luck—and had their ears boxed to cool their daring.

Mocassin Gap, the gateway to the Indian country. Here the company waited. The heavy flatboats carrying not only whole families but their household goods and in some cases their livestock as well, required deep water. Until the late autumn rains came to swell the streams there was nothing to do but wait. Patience became strained, tempers sharpened. Then finally, with Christmas only a few days off, Colonel Donelson gave the long awaited signal.

His flagship, the *Adventure*, cast off and went lumbering out into the stream. A square sail rigged up bravely well in the prow, billowed out like a beckoning hand. Smoke curled from the cabin chimney, attesting to the practical hearth within and a certain amount of warmth for anyone wishing to squeeze into the limited space. There were fifty souls

aboard the *Adventure*. Most of the young people ranged the
deck, watching as another and another of the thirty boats
that made up the flotilla took its place in line and began
moving down the Holston. In the stern, men took turns at
the long curved sweeps, keeping the boats in mid-stream.
Muskets stood ready. So into the Indian country, bravely,
with hope and determination.

Sleet hissed against the *Adventure's* cabin on Christmas
Eve and the fireplace sputtered like an angry hen. Someone
suggested singing carols, but the plan was abandoned as too
dangerous after an arrow from an unseen bow had fallen on
the deck earlier in the evening. One of the Robertson children was ill; the question of the moment was not Christmas
but whether or not to make camp ashore. Considering the
storm, however, it seemed best not to attempt a landing.

So, though the boats were moored close to the shore, the
night was spent in the cabin. Children fretted and cried in
the stale air; groups alternately dozed and moved about the
cramped quarters, thinking of other Christmases, wondering whether or not they had been foolhardy to risk so much
for the promised Utopia somewhere at their journey's end.

Rachel "had a way" with babies, the women said, so when
she was not cradling one of her own nieces or nephews,
crooning, patting its back, stilling its restlessness, she was
doing the same thing for some other child while its mother
snatched an hour's nap. Once she nodded herself over the
baby she had quieted, and woke with a start to find her
father looking down at her. Water streamed from his cloak

and cap and his beard was matted against his cheeks, but he was smiling as he stooped to pat her shoulder.

"My Rachel, my good child," he said softly, then turned and a sheet of snow-specked rain blew against her briefly as he opened the door and went out again to take up his post in the night. Some time later she thought she heard shrill voices screaming far back in the flotilla. Then she fell asleep again, comfortably certain that what she had heard was the wailing of the storm. Papa was keeping watch; they were safe.

Safe for the moment, perhaps, for the raiding party of savages had been small and was quickly repulsed without casualties. But the months that lay ahead were filled with terror to try to the utmost the courage of the entire party. Provisions ran low; game, usually so plentiful, seemed to have disappeared, and on a day in February when searing cold added its sting to all the other misery, a feeble shout was heard from one of the boats well back in the line. It was relayed to Colonel Donelson who ordered the flotilla stopped and ran back himself to see what was wrong.

A man stood at the side of the boat, holding himself upright by clinging to a pile of household goods lashed on deck, for support. His face was livid, his eyes dull, and even from the shore Colonel Donelson could see the blotches. Smallpox!

As the horror of the situation dawned upon the Colonel, he knew only one course lay open to him: the plague-infested boat must leave the flotilla, must drop back, lest the entire company become infected. And on the rocky banks, naked, coppery figures crept closer; unwinking, beady eyes watched. When the lone boat with its twenty-eight passengers, many of them desperately sick, was quite alone, drifting slowly with the current, the yelling horde poured down the bank.

Far up ahead, those aboard the *Adventure* and the other boats heard the gunfire, the screams of the captives. Not one of the twenty-eight escaped. Those who were not killed were marched into captivity and not seen again.

Rachel turned to Jane, her eyes dark with pity. "Oh, Janie, those poor people! The Stuarts—think—their baby! Oh, listen!"

Jane clapped her hands over her ears. "Stop it! Stop talking about it or I'll go crazy! I don't want to listen!" she quavered, close to hysteria. "I don't care if the Stuarts *are* back there! It's their own fault!"

"Janie Donelson!"

"Well, it is. They might be safe back home. So might we if—if Papa and Colonel Robertson and all those men at Williamsburg hadn't talked so much about settling the West. Who *cares* if the West is settled or not? I don't. What'll become of us? I make no doubt we'll be spinsters. Or if not, then mayhap you'll marry a scout like Daniel Boone and spend your days alone the way Mistress Boone does, waiting for him to come home. Not me . . ." she tossed her head, and Rachel, though she was seething with anger at hearing her father criticized even indirectly, thought for an instant how beautiful her tall, green-eyed, golden-haired sister was.

Then, "You ask *me* to stop talking, Janie," she exploded

finally, "but you ought to be ashamed, just *ashamed* to run on about getting married or being a spinster or whatever, when people you know are in such terrible trouble close by!"

Rachel's cheeks were scarlet, her lower lip thrust out, her dark eyes blazing. The two girls were standing in the prow, as far as possible from the dreadful sounds borne on the wind from the rear. Suddenly Jane sat down on a cask and covered her face with her hands. "Oh, Rachel, you're such a sweet, daft darling," she cried between laughter and tears. "I know I'm horrid, but I—I reckon I'm just not a pioneer. You're like Papa. You like people. I don't . . . not all people, just some. You think this . . ." she made a sweeping gesture that included the flatboat, the river, and the forest-clogged bluffs that hemmed it in . . . "is adventure. To me it's a nightmare, all of it. I'd not have Mama and Papa know, but it's the truth."

To pretty Jane, and to many another young woman, the treks into the wilderness which made America, were all nightmares. But to Rachel Donelson, child though she was, the conquering of each heartbreaking mile was a challenge met, a silent, powerful enemy overcome. Adventure was not quite the word to describe Rachel's feeling; accomplishment perhaps, like successfully turning the heel of an enormous sock she was knitting, or curbing a particularly headstrong pony she was riding.

Terror and grief she felt beyond her years. It had been Rachel who for two days could not swallow food when she heard that young Mrs. Peyton's day-old baby had been killed by a Cherokee arrow. Yet Rachel's was the stalwart, clear-eyed outlook of the typical pioneer woman who, given ever so brief a respite from hardship, could laugh defiance in the face of yet more suffering to come. Such was twelve-year-old Rachel Donelson, merry, tender, patient with the younger children; a romp and a ringleader among the girls and boys her own age; yet grown-ups found the Donelson's youngest daughter someone to be relied upon, prudent, resourceful under stress.

The long winter months with their brief daylight and their long nights, stretched on and on. Indian forays continued, illness of one kind or another struck down whole families at a time. Miraculously though, the big Donelson family and their thirty slaves escaped. So they came at last to that sunny cool morning in May, 1780 when the *Adventure* slid almost eagerly, it seemed, into the mud and marsh grass which marked the landing at the Great Salt Lick. The voyage was over.

(Rachel sighed, tucked her cheek against Jane's shoulder and fell asleep.)

Chapter 2

A MEETING

"They got Tom!"

"Keep down! Keep down, Andy!"

Robert Jackson, dark-eyed, sixteen and not much taller than his gangling thirteen year old brother, raised himself cautiously on his outspread hands and peered through the bushes. Yes, the British dragoons were galloping off, forcing Cousin Tom Crawford's big black stallion to gallop along with them. As long as Tarleton's men were in the neighborhood it paid to be careful, and Cousin Tom had not been. Now Robert's greatest problem was Andy.

Andrew Jackson was very tall for his age, his long, thin, freckled face part and parcel of his general angularity. Coarse blond hair tinged with red, formed a ragged cap that sat his head jauntily and the blue eyes that twinkled from under his heavy, sun-bleached brows held a quality of combined puckishness and deep candor that was most engaging. He was fierce in his loyalties and his hatreds; his temper was quick, and an injustice, real or fancied, done him or anyone dear to him, was sure to bring down a tempest on the offender.

On one occasion a group of pranksters loaded a musket with an enormous charge of powder and handed it to Andrew, inviting him to shoot at a target. He was justly proud of his marksmanship and took the heavy musket in good faith, eager to show these seasoned frontiersmen what he could do.

The kick of the gun sent the boy sprawling and a roar of laughter went around the group. Andrew scrambled to his feet, white with anger, his fists clenched.

"Stop that laughing—all of you!" he screamed. "I'll kill the first one I see crackin' a smile!"

The laughter stopped. Andrew's reputation as a savage fighter, his steely strength that of two, was well known, and his tormentors never doubted that he meant what he said.

But that had been months earlier. Now he pulled himself up to a kneeling position in spite of his brother's warning and looked about him. "They're gone, Bob," he said at last. "Come on. Yonder's a house and I'm hungry."

The boys, despite their youth, were fighting with the route would be led by Colonel James Robertson, one of the American army. They made their way across the fields to a distant farmhouse and were enjoying hot grits and side meat when there came a knocking at the door. Now what? Was this only a neighbor come to borrow a cup of sourdough? Or had they been followed after all and was that business-like thumping on the door a soldier's?

Andy had half risen when the door was flung open from the outside and a party of British dragoons filed in, sabers drawn. Robert and Andrew were arrested, the house was ransacked and Andrew ordered to clean the muddy boots of the officer in command. And here young Jackson's temper was his undoing. He flatly refused to clean the boots and the officer, with an oath, swung his saber high and brought it down on the hand Andrew instinctively had flung up to protect his face. The hand was cut to the bone and a glancing blow struck his temple, inflicting a long gash down the side of his cheek and across the bridge of his nose.

"So you 'must insist on being treated as a prisoner of war,' eh, my young cock o' th' walk?" scoffed the dragoon. "Well, that you shall be. Tie up that hand of yours, then forward march!"

There was no choice but to obey. But what of Robert? What were they doing to him? Seething with anger and a sense of having been taken advantage of, Andrew fell in line. A march of forty miles lay ahead, a march with neither food nor water. When the famished boy tried to scoop up a handful of water from the creeks they crossed, his hand was struck down. At last, drugged with weariness and pain, he reached the British camp at Camden on the Wateree River. There was comfort in knowing that Robert would be in the same prison even though they did not see each other.

Days dragged into weeks while the British and the Americans, locked in a seesawing battle in the meadow directly behind the prison, brought to a close that part of the Revolution which was fought in the southern part of the United States.

At about the same time at Mount Vernon Martha Washington was waving good-by to her son, Jackie Custis, as he galloped off to war with his beloved step-father, George Washington. In Virginia, too, at Monticello, Patsy Jefferson and her mother were driving away in one direction while her father, Thomas Jefferson, warned by Jack Jouitt, rode off in another just before Tarleton's raiders arrived, bent on capturing the author of the Declaration of Independence. And in those last weeks of the war, in the prison at Camden, South Carolina, Andrew Jackson was finding the treatment harsh. He shuddered away from the unsavory dishes put before him; his shoes and coat were stolen; he lived in filth. Then smallpox struck. Robert who had received a saber wound from the same officer who had struck Andrew, was already suffering from the disease when his younger brother developed it, though in milder form.

About this time, with the end of hostilities in sight, there was an exchange of prisoners, and one day into the enemy prison yard rode plucky, blue-eyed, little Mrs. Jackson to ask for permission to take her sick boys home. The British commander, probably touched by the gallant mother's courage, granted her request and the three set out for the Crawford homestead on the Catawba River, not far from Charles Town.

Feverish, bareheaded, in rags, Andrew trudged along leading two horses. On one rode his mother, on the other Robert, shouting in delirium, unconscious of his companions or his whereabouts. And on the pitiful little cavalcade the cold autumn rain fell in driving gusts.

Robert lived only long enough to reach home. When Andrew finally was able to be up following his own severe relapse, Mrs. Jackson remembered other sick boys she had seen in Camden and Charles Town. Making a packet of a change of clothing, she joined several other patriotic women of the community and set out.

Andrew watched her go with a sinking heart. Death had taken his two brothers—Hugh, the eldest, had died on the march—and now his mother, the mother he loved so, who understood him and gave him the gentle counsel he knew he needed, now this beloved mother was deliberately going into the very vale of contagion where plague daily took the lives of hundreds. The boy, weakened by weeks of illness himself, was beside himself with the dread of losing her. What was it she had said at parting? "Andy, never tell a lie nor take what is not yours nor sue for slander. Settle these cases yourself." He must try to remember that. So courageous she was—so very dear!

Her small packet of untouched clothes was returned to him. That was all. Elizabeth Jackson had contracted small-pox shortly after reaching Charles Town—soon to be re-named Charleston—and two days later was among the dead who were buried in a common grave.

Stunned and shaken by the realization that he was now wholly alone, Andy sat looking at the little packet so carefully wrapped and tied by the mother he would not see again. Dully he recalled things she had told him of her own youth in Ireland, of the voyage across the North Atlantic with her young husband, Andrew Jackson. Her sisters Mary, Sarah, Margaret and Jane, had come to America earlier and were married and in homes of their own in the region known as the Waxhaws, along the borders of North and South Carolina. Here, too, the young Jacksons staked out their farm and built their house. Though never a rich man, Jackson prospered and the two little sons, Hugh and Robert, born to him and his Elizabeth, knew the warmth and security of a happy home. When a promised little sister should arrive—ah, what a day that would be for the Jacksons!

But the whole bright pattern of the household changed in the flip of crow's wing when the sturdy farmer injured himself while pulling tree stumps and in less than a week was dead.

Because the first spring thaws had begun, the roads were treacherously slippery and the jolting drive to the little cemetery was painfully slow. Night fell as the mourners turned homeward and when the wagon in which Elizabeth and her little boys rode, reached the farm of her sister and brother-in-law, Jane and James Crawford, it seemed wiser for her not to attempt the long drive which still separated her from her own fireside.

Thus it was that two days later, March 15, 1767, another

brother instead of the promised sister, after all, came to join four-year-old Hugh and two-year-old Robert Jackson and was named Andrew for his father.

Aunt Jane Crawford was an invalid and there were eight children in the big square farmhouse in the Waxhaws; so Elizabeth Jackson and her three little sons stayed on and Elizabeth took over the management of the household. The years drew on. Elizabeth kept her own rich hundred acres and sent Andrew to the one really good school in the district. Neither Hugh nor Robert was a student, but the youngest boy had learned to read when he was five and his mother was determined he should have every opportunity for an education she could give him. Many of the frontiersmen in the Waxhaws could not read, so as the Revolution moved southward and word of victories and defeats became increasingly important to the citizens, it was nine-year-old Andy Jackson who acted as public reader and, standing on his Uncle James's front stoop, read aloud the news.

As the British moved on Charles Town, Mrs. Jackson and her boys found refuge in the home of distant cousins, the Wilsons, just across the North Carolina border. When Andrew saw his mother a refugee, fleeing before the invading troops of Cornwallis and Tarleton, hatred for the British became a fixation in the boy's pliant mind, which remained with him to the end of his life. He despised all things British. That his mother should be forced by *anyone* to leave her home was an act he would never forgive nor forget, and even the comparatively safe refuge of the Wilson farm in no way lessened his pent up fury at the enemy.

One morning his cousin, John Wilson, a mild mannered boy about his own age, saw Andrew chopping out weeds with a violence he could not understand and with a flow of language that frightened him.

"Cousin Andy," he inquired, sauntering up quietly and speaking in what he thought was a placating tone, "Why're you hackin' those weeds so tumultuous?"

Andrew whirled on him. "Weeds? Weeds, say you, Johnny? Those ain't weeds, they're every one a blasted British soldier! Weeds? Hmph! I *respect* weeds!" And he went back to his chopping. Johnny put his fingers in his ears and retreated. There is a story that years later he became a prominent clergyman and refused to vote for his hot-tempered cousin when Andrew ran for the Presidency.

Now that short stay at the Wilsons seemed long, long ago—almost another life, Andrew thought with a rueful smile, awkwardly fingering the knot of the cord that bound the packet of clothing. Now—well, there seemed nothing to do but to go away. No sense in staying here where memories and a loved ghost walked through the hours and the days were one long ache of loneliness. Better go away somewhere—anywhere. Suddenly tears stung his eyes and he quickly brushed his sleeve across them.

To be fourteen, alone and unhappy, this was a situation packed with hazards for a boy who was sensitive and quick tempered, living on the frontier. For a time at least, Andrew's love of knowledge and the thought of his mother's pride in his scholarship took him to several schools. Then for six months or more he worked as apprentice to a saddler. It was to the creak of leather and with the reek of curing acids and oils in his nostrils that he one day read a letter from Carrifergus, Ireland. His grandfather, Hugh Jackson, a weaver, had died and had left him a legacy of about four hundred pounds.

Andrew must have stared at the letter in unbelieving amazement. Four hundred pounds! What couldn't one do with four hundred pounds! Cracky! It could mean college, or again all those badly needed improvements on the farm which now was his. He needed advice badly but where find it? He was over fifteen and presently sixteen while he roamed about, keeping himself busy with any occupation that came his way. He had been a reckless but expert horseman from the time he first had been able to hoist himself to the back of a rangy grass pony. His judgement of horseflesh was excellent and he was called upon constantly to appraise horses, so it was only natural that one of his first major investments should be a beautiful thoroughbred. This in turn called for a handsome saddle.

After that he must be more suitably dressed, so young Mr. Jackson outfitted himself—rather extravagantly. Then he viewed himself critically. A broad streak of common sense in the boy somehow cleared his vision and showed him a handsomely dressed young man with not enough education to carry on the simplest business transaction. The shock of that knowledge steadied him and sent him for several

profitable semesters to Queen's Museum in Charlotte. Then
restlessness overcame him again.

There was the whole wide world to see. He must move
on. So Andrew came to Salisbury, North Carolina, a town
comprised of not more than fifty families and considerable
wealth. There was in Salisbury everything to entice and
enchant a lonely, untried boy with his pockets full of money:
horseracing, cock-fighting, card-playing, all the devices.

A certain aristocracy flourished in Salisbury, an aristocracy
with a Tidewater flavor, reminding one of the Dandridges,
the Washingtons, the Jeffersons. Among the ladies of this
select little community there was some raising of the eye-
brows at the behavior of the young man from the Waxhaws
in his expensive clothes who was squandering much too
much of his time on questionable diversions.

But if, with the Irish exuberance of his father, he plunged
recklessly into whatever chancy enterprises came his way,
yet here again that broad streak of common sense which he
must have had from his mother, led him to begin reading
law. With his fiery temper, the young South Carolinian
possessed a magnetic personality, and his deference and court-
liness in all his dealings with women won him instant and
lasting friendships among the more conservative people of
the town. One woman in trying to describe young Mr. Jackson's charm, called it "a presence" which everyone felt
instantly when they came within the orbit of his warm
personality.

For a time he was in the office of Spruce Macay, an at-

torney of Salisbury, but the renowned jurist, Colonel John
Stokes, was watching him and soon Andrew was reading
law in the Colonel's office. The legal experience he gained
was invaluable and in 1787 when he was just twenty years
old, Andrew Jackson was admitted to the bar.

Good fortune was smiling on him at this time. He won
several cases almost at once and then, while trying still
another in Martinsville, he was invited to visit an old class-
mate, John McNairy. John was a well-to-do young man
whose father was a close friend of the Governor of North
Carolina. John himself had been elected recently to the
Superior Court bench of what was known as the Western
District of the state, and John in turn appointed his friend
Andrew Jackson public prosecutor.

Young Judge McNairy's jurisdiction spread out across a
vast territory and court convened in the more important
settlements in the District. Fees seldom were paid in money
but often in land, one of the cheapest commodities; so before
he was twenty-one, Andrew Jackson was a landowner of
considerable importance.

It was on a September afternoon in 1788 that Andrew
reined in his horse on a bluff overlooking the Cumberland
Valley. So much beauty, so much wild green grandeur burst-
ing upon him suddenly, left him sitting motionless in the
saddle, stunned by the magnificent panorama of mountain
and forest, of valley and winding river. And yonder must be
Fort Nashborough, he thought, sighting the cluster of buildings in the middle distance which one day would be the city

of Nashville. He spoke to his horse and began the slow descent. Here, he knew, was the most beautiful country he ever had seen.

A wagon train of pioneers moving westward had come into the settlement just ahead of him and the one tavern was crowded to capacity. What had his friend, John Overton, said about Fort Nashborough? "If you find no room there, Andy, try the Donelson station. You'll have to cross the river and take the road north for about seven miles, but it's worth the trouble."

So now Andrew crossed the river and wound northward along the fern-edged trail toward the Donelson stockade. Arrived, he dismounted and knocked at the massive gate. Silence answered, broken only by the drowsy clucking of hens and the sound of a distant rich contralto voice singing. He knocked again and the singing stopped. Then he heard the sound of hurrying steps and the gate swung slowly open.

He found himself facing a girl with dark eyes, a girl in blue linsey-woolsey who held down her waving black hair in the wind with one hand while with the other she maneuvered the latch of the gate. A dimple touched her left cheek briefly when she smiled and her voice when she spoke held a quality of gentle promise that was music to the weary man.

"I am Andrew Jackson, ma'am," he began, twisting his tricorn awkwardly. "John Overton said. . . ."

"Of course. John's spoken of you often, Mr. Jackson. Come in. I'm Mrs. Donelson's daughter, Rachel Robards." She stepped back, opening the gate wide.

Chapter 3

HARRODSBURG

There was never a wasted moment inside the big Donelson log house. Cooking, baking, preserving, spinning, weaving, sewing, cleaning, the work of one day met the following day's incoming tasks at evening. Only for a few brief hours late at night was there a complete stop to the endless activity. Then the fires were banked, the house seemed to yawn, stretch, and fall asleep . . . with one eye open.

Rachel had been busy all morning helping Francie, the cook, with preserving. Wild blackberries were ripe and great sagging baskets of the purple fruit had stood in orderly rows on the kitchen work table and the floor beneath it. Now the jam was ready to pour into the big brown crocks, to be sealed with oiled paper and stored in the fruit cellar under the kitchen. Unlike fruit which boiled only a few moments in its syrup, jam need not be sealed while hot. Boiled for several hours, it could be poured and sealed when it was easier to handle. So Rachel would wait until Francie had finished other tasks. Meanwhile, she could sit in the shade for a few moments, then go up and change into a fresh dress for the afternoon.

The day had dawned cool, and she had put on a dress of linsey-woolsey. Now it had turned very warm. She found an over-turned tub on the shady side of the spring house and pushed it closer to the wall, sat down on it and leaned back. She closed her eyes and let the wind blow through her hair and across the soft pale hollow of her tanned throat. Just to dream for a moment—to hope.

How many years had it been since the morning she and her mother had come ashore from the *Adventure* and had been glad to see Hector bringing in the wood for their first fire? Nine years, a long time, and oh, how much had happened since then!

That first homemaking had been so futile for Indians had interrupted the gathering of the first harvest of badly needed corn and cotton, and the following year had brought much sickness and ever growing threats of massacre. The Creeks, Chickasaws, and Chicamaugas roamed the valley of the Cumberland, scalping, killing, plundering. Finally, it seemed to Colonel Donelson that for the time being at least, he must not subject his family to such hazards when a less dangerous

location was not too far away. His son John had married and
moved to Kentucky, so now to Mercer County, Kentucky,
went Colonel Donelson and his large family where they
settled not far from Harrodsburg, near John and his pretty
Mary.

Why, Rachel wondered now nine years later, had Kentucky seemed so safe? Her fourteenth, fifteenth, and six-
teenth years were passed under a black cloud of anxiety.
True, they had been spent in the very shadow of the big
fort at Harrodsburg, but scarcely a day passed without its
tragedy. How the Donelson family escaped is one of the mys-
teries of American pioneer history, for the men of the family
were constantly in the thick of every fray, and the women as
much exposed to capture or torture by roving bands of
Cherokees and Shawnees as the others. Still they escaped,
and by the time Rachel was seventeen and Colonel Donelson
felt they might with safety return to the Cumberland, at
least one member of the family preferred to stay in Kentucky.

Rachael Donelson had grown from a merry romp of a
little girl into a beautiful young woman whose sparkling,
warm magnetism was tempered with a new dignity and
whose lovely contralto voice, singing the old ballads, stirred
more than one young frontiersman's heart. Rachel had more
than her share of suitors, but she was not ready for marriage,
she said quite frankly, and sent them on their way. Then
one day not long before the Donelsons were to return to
the Cumberland, handsome Captain Lewis Robards came
calling.

Sitting in the shadow of the spring house, eyes closed, Rachel felt her cheeks burn at the memory of that first call from Lewis. He was so handsome, ten years older than she, and he sat his mettlesome horse with such ease, his eyes so frankly admiring as they met hers. Within a fortnight they were betrothed and in the spring of 1785 Rachel Donelson became Rachel Robards and went to live in the rather imposing Robards house in Harrodsburg where Lewis's mother welcomed her.

Those were the happy days! The Robards family was an old one, Mrs. Robards a Virginian with all the gentleness of the Tidewater in her speech and manner. She and Rachel loved each other on sight and the bride wondered a little at the shadow of unhappiness she saw in the older woman's eyes. What should make her unhappy, Rachel wondered. She was one of the most loved and honored women in the settlement; her son obviously adored her; her home was probably the most comfortable in the region. What was wrong? Finally, with her family preparing to leave, Rachel put the thought from her as a figment of her imagination. Her hand in her husband's, she waved happily from the porch as her brother William led the Donelson clan down the road to join a party bound for the Cumberland and her father turned his horse's head toward Virginia. His business completed there, he promised to stop by for a visit before joining his family at their station near Fort Nashborough.

Rachel felt a warm glow in her heart at the thought of that visit. She would be entertaining Papa in her own home, she, Rachel Robards. She smiled up at Lewis and he tightened his arm about her shoulder as they stood there together, waving, a picture of happiness. Then, one evening a few weeks later, Rachel knew the reason for the shadow in her mother-in-law's eyes, knew it as her own dark eyes clouded and her heart seemed suddenly incased in ice.

The young Robards had been invited to a housewarming at the far end of the settlement, and Rachel, in a dress of deep red wool, was a picture of gay, sparkling beauty. Lewis, as he held her cloak, laid his cheek for an instant against hers.

"You're too lovely to share with all those backwoods yokels, darling." he whispered. "Come, stay at home. We'll sing ballads together instead, or—or I'll teach you to play *bezique*. Come, please. . . ."

They were facing a mirror and Rachel laughed happily at the reflection of their two faces so close together and shook her head. "La, I'd rather stay at home with you, Lewis," she answered, laying her hand against his cheek, "but you know we cannot do that. They're not yokels—just backwoodsmen—like us—and they're counting on us, dear. We'll have to go, but we can come home early."

She saw him stiffen and draw back, but his voice was entirely friendly when he countered, "Promise? We come home early?"

She cuffed his ear playfully and began fastening her cloak and drawing its hood over her curls. "Promise," she said. So they set out across the melting spring snow to the housewarming.

Fiddles were scraping already when they arrived and shouts of, "Here they are!" "Here're Cap'n Robards and Mistress Rachel!" went up on all sides. Someone took Rachel's cloak; someone else removed her fur-bordered moccasins that were the galoshes of the day.

It was easily seen that Rachel Robards was an enormously popular young woman. Her frank, unaffected nature endeared her to the women; the men found her dark beauty, her quick wit, her infectious laughter irresistible. And Rachel accepted all the friendliness offered her with the light-hearted joy of a child. Hers was the innocence of the undesigning and it kept her inviolate, a lovely creature to whom everyone seemed a friend; who gave generously of herself; without whom no frontier gathering, whatever its size, seemed complete.

Tonight she was at her best. She was newly wed to the man she loved; every mirror, every admiring glance told her she was looking extremely well; fiddles were tuning up and her feet in their bronze kid slippers were eagerly tapping.

"Gentlemen, choose your partners for the Virginia Reel!"

A clatter of boots, and four bachelors went clumping and sliding across the floor to Rachel's side. But Lewis was there first.

"Mrs. Robards will dance this one with me, gentlemen," he said pleasantly as he caught her hand and as they took their places, "Don't these fools know that a man dances the first dance with his lady?" he added, not lowering his voice or seeming to care who heard him.

Rachel laughed up at him merrily and laid her finger tips on his lips. But Lewis seemed intent on something beyond her line of vision. He did not join her laughter or take note of her gesture. In the figures of the dance naturally Rachel had many partners; and afterward there were the romping singing games with much stamping and hand clapping; then another square dance. By that time supper was in preparation.

Hewn logs athwart crude "horses" were covered with hand woven cloths, forming one long table flanked by sturdy benches borrowed from the schoolhouse for the occasion. The women helped in placing the hearty food—baked ham, corn dumplings, the jellies and pickles and dried apple tarts. These, with generous pots of coffee, made a delectable climax to the rollicking evening. Rachel, flushed, her great eyes dancing, carried a heavy pot of coffee around the table, filling the cups, leaning carefully not to stain the white cloth. Across from her, another young matron placed dishes of wild celery and cut wedges of thin crusty corn bread which she distributed, a wedge to a plate, as she circled the table.

Suddenly, as she straightened from filling a cup, Rachel was seized with a strange feeling of unease. Where was Lewis? The other men were standing about the table, laughing, jokingly speeding the women with their preparations. But Lewis was not among them. Not quite knowing why it should be so, Rachel realized her hands were shaking, her heart pounding unaccountably. She went to the hearth, hastily set the pot down and looked about her.

The house, a good sized cabin of several rooms, offered opportunities for seclusion. One of these was a deeply recessed window ell beyond and behind the great fireplace. Rachel skirted the fireplace, pushed her way through a knot of young people gathered about an amateur magician— "Look here, Rachel," Watch this, Mrs. Robards," "Here's something to see, ma'am,"—and turned the corner of the ell.

Lewis sat there chatting with a notoriously disagreeable man, a relative of the host who had taken advantage of his kinship by presenting himself, uninvited, at the party. He was a boor, a drunkard, and a braggart, the very type of man she knew Lewis detested. Yet here sat her husband, stony-faced, listening to the man's recitation of his endless abilities.

"Lewis," her voice sounded strained, rough, and she cleared her throat apologetically, "we have supper about ready. Won't you come in now? You've never seen such a beautiful ham," she added lamely when he seemed not to hear her, and made futile little wavering gestures toward the table.

Finally her husband shifted his gaze from the man across from him and eyed her for a long moment. Then, "I thought it was decided before we came that we'd leave early," he observed, making no move to get up. Studied insolence was in every tone, every angle of his sprawling body as he slid lower in his chair.

Stung by his rudeness, particularly before the stranger, Rachel parried. "I know it, Lewis, but we can scarcely leave before supper. Besides," she put her hand on his arm and smiled determinedly into his sullen face, "we're all having such a good time it would be a pity to go in the midst of it. Come, we'll leave directly after supper if you want to. . . ."

"We shall? Well, now really, how kind of you, Rachel," he drawled.

He got slowly to his feet and his hand on her arm as he led her back to the feast was like a steel trap. Behind them she heard the stranger snicker, and turned sick with anger. This outrage Lewis would permit—would be a part of!

She tried for her hostess's sake to eat the delicious food heaped on her plate, but found she could not. Instead, she watched, fascinated, while her husband, chuckling amiably at something the pretty girl on his other side was saying, seemed to be enjoying his supper immensely. Bewilderment added to Rachel's wretchedness. How could Lewis take such obvious delight in hurting her? And what had she done to deserve it?

Shortly after supper the Robards started home. The ground was uneven and treacherously slippery. Even so, Rachel winced and tried to withdraw her arm from Lewis's vice-like grip.

"Lewis, please—" she said, when finally his fingers bit too deeply.

He dropped her arm so suddenly that she almost fell in the inky darkness. Lewis continued to stride along, making no move to help her as she groped her way alone. After they had walked in silence for several rods he spoke, quietly, evenly, but his voice unexpectedly piercing the silence of the midnight frontier, had the volume and quality of a shot.

"You seem to hold your home and your husband very lightly, Rachel," he began. "We were to have left that wretched gathering early. . . ." His pace had quickened with his speech which was racing now and, slipping and stumbling along beside him, Rachel finally reached out and clung to his sleeve. She was at a disadvantage and the knowledge made her own voice shrill.

"But certainly we couldn't have come sooner, Lewis. You know that . . . ."

"Oh, no? And why not? Because you enjoyed it, actually enjoyed it—or seemed to. You clapped and stamped and shrieked like any tavern wench. Did you find the attentions of those—those wilderness rowdies so flattering that you could forget completely that you are a married woman and not an unmannered country girl?"

"Lewis, hush! Don't shout so! The whole settlement will hear. How *can* you say such things?" Rachel was running long beside him now as his pace made it necessary, and her voice came in quavering gasps. "I *didn't* shriek or act like a tavern wench as you say I did. You know as well as I do that those singing games all call for clapping and stamping and calling out signals. What was I supposed to do? Leave the room? As for enjoying it, I did. But I thought you did, too, only after a while I couldn't find you and. . . ."

"Well, I didn't enjoy it. I hated all of it. No man enjoys watching his wife make a cheap spectacle of herself, flirting with every Tom, Dick, and. . . ."

Rachel stopped so abruptly that for a moment in the dark Lewis thought she had slipped and fallen. He continued for a few paces, then stopped and looked back.

"Well? Are you coming or not?" Petulance and dawning shame made him shout in spite of himself. Rachel stood still, listening to the pounding of blood in her ears, weak with humiliation and shock. Lewis walked back to her and repeated his question. " . . . Are you?"

At last Rachel forced herself to answer. "Yes—I'm coming because I have no choice. If I had I wouldn't. I can only say shame — shame on you, Lewis!"

She cried herself to sleep that night, and though her husband's apology was abject and sincere, she knew with a sick heart that the fine fabric of her marriage had been sullied and cheapened. She wondered what her father and brothers would have thought at Lewis's abusive language, wondered and determined they never should know.

Old Mrs. Robards was quick to sense the tension as the days passed, to note Rachel's swollen eyes. "Dear child, take courage," she said, putting her warm hand over the girl's icy one. "I know things are not going well with you and Lewis, and it is my fault — I should have told you. Jealousy is a sickness and my boy has suffered from it all his life. I've

wanted to warn you but the right moment never seemed to
come, and now you've been hurt. But be patient, Rachel. The
very fact that he loves you so makes him unreasonably jeal-
ous. I make no excuses for him . . ." the gentle voice broke
. . . "but ever since he was a little boy I've known how much
unhappiness he was storing up and I've tried to shield him
from his own worst enemy—himself. So forgive much, dear.
Lewis needs you, he needs you more than you know."

Rachel put her arms around the little figure and laid her
cheek against the white hair. She was aboard the *Adventure*
again, rubbing unguent on small chapped hands, comforting
weary and frightened children. "I'll keep him happy, I promise," she soothed, and never was a promise more sincerely
given.

However, the month that followed wiped Rachel's mind
clean of everything but the tragedy it held. Colonel Donelson, true to his word, did stop off in Harrodsburg on his
way to Fort Nashborough, and for several days Rachel gave
herself up to the joy of listening to his tales and convincing
him of her own happiness. Lewis was charming, and the Colonel kissed his youngest daughter good-by in a glow of sat-
isfaction. His baby girl was safe, married to as fine a man as
any father would ask for his best loved child.

The true story of what happened to Colonel Donelson
probably never will be told. That he was ambushed and
killed almost within sight and sound of home, either by Indians or highwaymen, was the tragic news brought to Rachel
a month later.

At first she refused to believe it. Papa — gone. Her mind refused to accept the truth. She wanted to run through the woods —calling his name, sure that in some sun-splattered alley of giant trees she would find him. Papa — no! Her grief roused all that was best in Lewis, his chivalry, his tenderness, and for several months a melancholy peace descended on the Robards household. And in the peace Rachel's spirits revived and her sympathy for every living suffering being.

So when one morning a young surveyor stopped by to ask for a drink of water, she invited the tired boy to rest on the vrandah. He accepted. She sat facing him across the length of the top step, shelling peas for the noonday dinner while he told her about his mother and sisters in North Carolina, when Lewis came riding in from the plantation.

Rachel introduced them and took her vegetables into the house, reminding herself to suggest to Mrs. Robards that it might be nice to invite the young surveyor to stay for dinner. Such hospitality was common in the early days of the country, was, in fact, taken for granted. Rachel was so certain of her mother-in-law's assent that she did not hurry but stopped to put the peas in a kettle before going to Mrs. Robard's room.

Chancing to look from the window as she crossed the hall, she saw the boy walking quickly away from the house. There was no need to ask why he had gone. Lewis's tight-lipped, speechless fury all that day and the next made it plain how great his resentment had been to find her talking with a stranger in his absence and on such friendly terms. His mother had called his senseless jealousy a sickness. It was, indeed, Rachel thought sadly, wondering how in the face of so much real trouble he could let pettiness ruin their lives.

Indians were again menacing the region — not big war parties, but small bands that plundered and burned and killed. Harrodsburg closed its shutters early and families with more than one grown man in them considered themselves lucky. Mrs. Robards was delighted when a distant cousin, John Overton, a young lawyer on his way west to the Cumberland country, stopped for a visit. Lewis was very fond of his kinsman, held his scholarly mind in great respect, and oddly enough encouraged Rachel to show him every courtesy. Truly, she thought, was there ever such an illogical man as Lewis Robards?

However, it was not hard to be kind to the shy, awkward young man, and Rachel liked him at once. He was slight, with pale gray eyes peering through spectacles which he wore far down his nose. A heavy mane of hair, so light as to be virtually white, swept back from a high forehead, giving him the appearance of a somewhat worried young mystic. John responded to Rachel's cousinly ministrations with an appreciation that was touching. And she who was never so content as when caring for someone who needed that care, sewed on buttons and mended socks with a quiet glow in her heart.

Lewis never tired of listening to Overton's tales of his experiences in the Carolinas, of the strange characters he met, the clients he represented, the grievances he listened to.

"But there's a lad from out the Waxhaws," he added one day, "Jackson's his name, Andrew Jackson, who has more right out-and-out laughable cases than any lawyer in the region. And just listening to him tell about them . . ." John slapped his knee and chuckled reminiscently. "If Jackson passes this way and knocks on your door, Lew, bid him welcome. He'll repay you a thousand fold in good fellowship alone. More than that, he's one of the best Indian fighters in the country. Remember the name — Jackson — Andrew Jackson."

Peace settled over the Robards household and Rachel prayed it would last. She and Lewis rode together occasionally and his pride in her skill at handling a spirited horse was a combined torment and delight to him. That she was a horsewoman of surpassing skill filled him with a kind of suffocating pride; that anyone beside himself should witness that skill he resented, all the more so because he was helpless to prevent it. After all, he had no monopoly on the roads. They seldom ventured off the well-traveled highway or far from the settlement for Indian depredations continued. Two men were found scalped in a hollow not far from Boonsborough, and a child picking berries just outside her own dooryard was carried into the wilderness by savages.

More able bodied men were urgently needed in and outside the Harrodsburg fort. It was at this time that Captain Peyton Short arrived in Harrodsburg and was given the name of Mrs. Robards as a lady at whose large house and ample table strangers with satisfactory credentials always were made welcome.

Peyton Short was a pompous little man, tactless, conceited, and dull, but well meaning. Rachel disliked him from the moment she saw him, but knowing what the presence of another officer in the house meant to her mother-in-law and to her own peace of mind, she tactfully laughed at his pointless jokes and tried to make him feel welcome.

Mrs. Robards, torn between gratitude for the Captain's presence and dread of the storm she felt was gathering, watched helplessly and prayed.

Rachel avoided the man when she could, but he lacked the delicacy to recognize her aloofness for what it was or to take to himself Lewis Robards's cutting sarcasms. Still stupidly feeding his ego, Peyton Short pictured himself a hero, foreordained to rescue a helpless woman from a boorish husband and redoubled his efforts to make himself, as he thought, indispensable to Rachel Robards.

Finally, in an inevitable upsurge of anger, Lewis ordered him from the house and made matters worse by airing his grievance to the entire settlement. John Overton might have saved his breath for all the good his efforts did to mollify Lewis.

"You're making a fool of yourself, Lew," he warned, "and you're not helping Rachel. No woman, especially a lady of Rachel's breeding and taste, wants to be made conspicuous; and that's what you're doing, Lew. Stop making such a row. Short's gone and good riddance. Now forget him."

And Rachel, too, once his fury had subsided enough to make him capable of listening, added her own plea. "Please stop telling everyone Captain Short was trying to break up our marriage," she begged. "That implies he must have had some encouragement from me, and you cannot believe that. I did my best not to be rude to the man, but your mother and John — *everyone* knows what a sorry specimen of manhood I thought he was. So if you do really love me, Lewis, stop all this nonsense about Peyton Short."

Watching her sensitive face, realizing perhaps how ridiculous he had been, Lewis did make an effort at self control. He might have succeeded if a letter in an unfamiliar hand had not arrived one morning addressed to Rachel.

Lewis opened the leather mail pouch, sorted the letters methodically, and at the one addressed to Rachel — stopped. Some minute, lightning-swift stab of prescience brought the angry color flooding to his face. He was alone on the verandah. Without a moment's hesitation he ripped the seal and unfolded the single sheet of paper. As he read, the color drained slowly from Lewis Robard's face, leaving it a greenish white.

"Rachel! Rachel!" It was not a shouted command but the high pitched, hysterical scream of a fanatic.

Peyton Short, in a moment of inexcusable audacity had written Rachel Robards a love letter. That she was as fully taken by surprise as was her husband meant nothing to Lewis. He was beyond reason. Through all the years that followed Rachel was to remember the senseless savagery of his accusations and his final judgement:

"You will get out of my house as soon as some member of

your family can come for you. For I won't have you under my roof!"

Then he was off to Virginia to challenge Short to a duel. Rachel could only hope one of her brothers would come quickly in answer to her urgent letter. To add to her wretchedness, the day after Lewis's return from Virginia — had he killed Peyton Short? Been wounded himself? — John Overton rode away down the Kentucky Road to the Cumberland. Rachel loved Mrs. Robards with the devotion of a daughter, but John, dear, nearsighted, understanding John had been a very rock of strength. In some strange fashion he always had managed to bring out the very best in Lewis, restoring Rachel's faith in the success of her marriage. Now, with John gone, she felt terribly alone.

Something had happened between Lewis and John as they stood at the gate just before Overton had left. What it was she could not guess. John seemed to have asked Lewis a question and the answer had been long and involved. A prolonged silence had followed, then John, ignoring Lewis's outstretched hand, had climbed into the saddle, wheeled his horse and had ridden out of sight.

It was Samuel, the best loved of her brothers, who came for Rachel two weeks later. Riding the horse her father had given her as part of her dowery, she followed her brother along the trails winding southwest. Samuel, dark, softspoken, reminding her much of their father, respected her reticence and they rode through the September forests for the most part in silence. Now and then Samuel, with a great

show of nonchalance, tossed off a bit of home news: Severn
had developed a bad cough — Mama was giving him tar and
sorgum to chew and he'd be better soon; Catherine was expecting another baby; Mama had had the stockade enlarged
until folks said it was the biggest station in the Cumberland;
crops were huge this year and there were several new calves
and colts. Thus the days passed, and at last they stopped before the heavy gates of the Donelson stockade.

Rachel slid from her horse and felt her mother's kiss
briefly on her cheek. But she held back her tears until they
were alone in her room with the door closed. Then Mrs.
Donelson held out her arms and Rachel went into them like
a lost, tired child.

"Oh, Mama — Mama — Mama— ." Tears choked her and
she could only cling to her mother, sobbing wordlessly.

"Darling — darling child — " the mother's hand smoothed
the dark hair, "try to think of all that has happened as a bad
dream," she soothed. "You're home, dear, home where we've
missed you so. Come, dry your tears." She slipped a handkerchief beneath the wet cheek on her shoulder. "I want you to
see all the building and changing we've been doing. If you
remember the stockade at all, you'll be surprised." She
hugged Rachel to her suddenly. "It's so good, so *good* to
have my girl with me again! Let's go down. We'll have
plenty of time later to talk about — other things."

Thus it was that Rachel came home. Quickly, easily, she
fitted into the family circle. Always she had been the favorite
"little sister;" now her unhappiness added a fillip to the

consideration shown her, and as the days passed and the pleasant bustle of the family comings and goings replaced the tension of the Robards home, some of Rachel's sparkle returned.

Jane, true to her own prediction, had waited and was just recently married to a man of means, Colonel Robert Hays. Their comfortable plantation and stockade were not far away and the sisters were constantly together, as they had been when they were children. May and Catherine, almost a generation older, were busy with their large and growing families. The same was true of John, William and Severn, and as they all lived more or less in the immediate neighborhood, that is within easy riding distance, Rachel found herself almost at once surrounded by a band of nieces and nephews ranging in age from a few days to within a few months of her own twenty-one years. Home, yes, this was home indeed; and one of the pleasantest of many surprises she discovered shortly after her return was that one of the guest cabins was occupied by John Overton! He came out to greet her when she knocked, peering through his thick-lensed glasses, his kind, homely face alight with pleasure.

"Rachel, Rachel Robards," he cried, seizing both her hands, "you are all this otherwise perfect place lacked! Now, by gracious, I'm settling right here! Been trying to make up my mind for days whether Nashville could support another lawyer. Now it's got to. Can't get used to the new name — been calling it Fort Nashborough so long."

"Of course it'll support you, John, no matter what its

name," she laughed. "It's mighty good to see you, and Mama is delighted to have you here — we all are. Have you met all the family? Aren't there a lot of them?"

John nodded yes to both questions and after a few moments of sharing her delighted comments on the station, he watched her go hurrying off across the enclosure, beautiful dark head held high, a basket containing delicacies for a sick field hand swinging on her arm. There was something so regal, so inviolable in her bearing that the man shrank with shame before the memory of Robards's abuse. Here was a woman to inspire the loftiest devotion and respect of all men, yet she had been driven from her husband's house branded a wanton.

The autumn days remained warm. Goldenrod, Queen Anne's lace and wild salvia strewed the meadows, seeming to rebuke the still, dark resignation of the forest where only an occasional falling leaf punctuated the summer's slow passing. Then on a warm, windy September afternoon in 1788 there had come the knocking at the stockade gate and Rachel opened it to admit Andrew Jackson.

Chapter 4

THE DONELSON STATION

ANDREW JACKSON walked beside Rachel across the yard to the house. So this was the Widow Donelson's station, famed the length of the frontier.

A barricade of logs, pointed at the top, surrounded the huge enclosure; not the all-too-familiar flimsy, straggling, irregular fence of many of the stations, but a solid wall of stout logs, deep sunk, clay chinked, and reinforced by interwoven iron bands, the whole the work of skilled craftsmen.

In the center of the compound stood the commodious, two-storied house; behind it the kitchen, the snug cabins for the house servants, the smoke house, supply shed, spring house and dairy. Behind these in turn, the barns and chicken run. At the front of the compound and flush with the wall itself, were the three guest cabins, each with its brightly curtained window and big outside chimney.

A compact little principality, thought Jackson, a home in every sense. The hens continued their drowsy afternoon clucking and singing; from the kitchen came the tempting smell of cooling blackberry jam, and as they stepped through the doorway into the cool interior he could not repress an exclamation of delight.

"Mmm! Mmm!"

Rachel turned. "Did you say something?"

He made a sweeping gesture which took in the whole room. "It's beautiful," he said simply, meaning the combination of heavy overhead beams, the floor covered with braided rugs, the stone fireplace with its gay chintz ruffle, the softly gleaming pewter on dresser shelves, the chests of dark mahogany from Virginia.

Rachel laughed softly. "I'm glad you like it, Mr. Jackson. We Donelsons have always thought Mama could make the inside of a tent beautiful. I reckon, though, all women who love their homes do the same thing, don't you?" She hesitated a moment, then, "Sit down and I'll call my mother. I know how glad she'll be to welcome you."

And indeed Mrs. Donelson was glad to welcome the tall, painfully thin young man who assured her so seriously that he was "an excellent shot, Ma'am, one of the best, they'll tell you in the settlements." She smiled at his eagerness, her motherly heart touched very deeply somehow by the freckles straggling across his nose and high cheek bones and by the childish way he had of ruffling his hair when he was perplexed until it stood out like a halo of fire. He looks like one of the younger martyrs, she thought, one in need of a hot bath and rest and plenty of good wholesome food.

"Of course you must stay, Mr. Jackson," she assured him, her hand on his arm, her brow puckered. "I'm just wondering where we can put you. The cabins are — Oh, I wonder — Mr. Overton speaks of you so often and his cabin is the first just inside the gate. I'm sure he wouldn't mind sharing . . ."

"Did you say Overton, John Overton, Ma'am? You mean John's here *now*?" Jackson's eyes danced, his mouth spread in a wide grin.

"Yes, he came in almost a month ago. He's found clients in Nashville, and I recall he said something about the possibility of your coming this way . . ."

Jackson's laugh rang out in a boyish shout of sheer delight. "Now I do declare! That rascal! Why, Ma'am, we'll make out fine in John's cabin if you'll have me. We'll both be too busy to be much under foot, I promise."

So Andrew Jackson came to live at the Donelson station. His horse unsaddled and stabled, his law books on the shelf beside John Overton's, he treated himself to the luxury of a bath and shave and fresh linen. He was drawing on his boots when Overton entered the cabin. For a moment the near-sighted little man stood peering into the semi-gloom, then with a whoop he sprang forward.

"Andy! Andy Jackson! By all that's good!"

"John!"

When the pommeling and back-slapping had ended, the two friends-of-the-trail sat down for a discussion of their

plans. Both men were young and ambitious. Jackson's reputation as an able lawyer had spread throughout the Cumberland, Overton was known for his tact and diplomacy in
handling difficult land tranactions. So what more natural
than that they should join forces, making an office of their
cabin in the Donelson stockade?

Standing in the doorway waiting for the call to supper,
Jackson nodded toward the blockhouse where candlelight
was beginning to twinkle in the deepening twilight.

"Mrs. Robards," he began. "You mentioned your kinsman,
Lewis Robards of Harrodsburg and his mother and his
wife Rachel. How does it happen that Mrs. Robards is
here? I mean is she visiting? Is her husband here, too? More
and more people are being drawn to the Cumberland, I
know, and I wondered."

So John Overton, weighing each word carefully, told the
wretched story of Rachel's humiliation. When he had finished, Jackson made no comment but the muscles of his
jaw tightened and a few moments later as they crossed the
enclosure to the house, Overton saw that his lips had become
the single thin line so characteristic a sign of his deep anger.

That night after they had gone to bed, Overton, drifting
into sleep, was roused by his bed-fellow's sudden outburst.

"The man should be flogged, John, I tell you, publicly
flogged!" he muttered, beating the quilt with his clenched
fist. No need to ask whom he meant. Andrew Jackson had
taken Rachel Robards's plight much to heart.

Autumn unfurled its gaudy pennants of crimson and gold

and flaming copper and marched through the forests and across the fields. Then overnight its glory was ended as snow-flecked winter rain came hissing down the slopes and left behind it the gaunt gray ghosts of summer's promise. At the Donelson station crops had been harvested, the weaving room hummed with the sound of spinning wheels and looms; winter fuel was piled high in sheds and against the kitchen wall, and the air was spicy with the scent of apple and peach butter baking in crocks in the vast ovens.

Through the fall and winter months Rachel found comfort in helping with her numerous young nieces and nephews. There were endless stockings to knit, skirts to be lengthened, fretful babies to quiet. And as she went from task to task her thoughts were with the handsome, irrascible husband she still loved.

One cold afternoon in mid-March John Overton eased himself into a chair near her as she sat before the fire weaving petticoat tapes on a small hand loom. "Rachel," he began, "I'm glad to find you alone . . .".

Rachel pushed back the loom and laid her shuttle beside it on the small tilt-top table at which she had been working. "You've heard from Lewis," she said quietly, impelled by a prescience she could not have explained.

He nodded. "A letter came this morning . . . Rachel, Lew has asked me to intercede for him. He begs you to forgive his stupidity and come back to him. I know you . . . ."

Rachel tossed her head and her cheeks were crimson, her eyes dark with indignation. "Forgive his stupidity, you say,

John. Lewis forgets that I spent hours trying with all patience to point out that dreadful stupidity to him. You were there, you heard and saw much of it . . . ."

"I know, Rachel, I know, but . . . ."

"How can he expect me to return to Harrodsburg where he made me so conspicuous, where every street urchin knew his opinion of me? How can he, John?"

Rachel's voice shook and Overton knew she was close to tears. She controlled herself by a mighty effort, though, and before he could answer she continued. "Lewis owns a good tract of land about five miles from here in Davidson County. I've thought of it so much, hoped so. . . . If he will come on here to the Cumberland and settle on his land, I'll put Harrodsburg and all that happened there out of my mind. I'll — I'll be Lewis's wife again. But not in Harrodsburg — not there — ever."

"May I write him that, Rachel? May I tell him to come?" John Overton's kind face glowed and impulsively he laid his hand over hers where it toyed with the shuttle on the table.

"Yes. Yes, tell him to come, John." For the first time in months Rachel found her eyes filling with tears as anger melted before the devotion she could not deny.

So John Overton wrote to Lewis Robards and Rachel watched the trail. It was May when finally Robards arrived, handsome, domineering, as careless in his manners as he was meticulous in his grooming. He charmed Rachel's family during the first days following his return — all but Samuel and Jane. Samuel could not forget Rachel's abject misery

when he had arrived in Harrodsburg to bring her home. As
for Jane, she eyed Robards with cool distaste as he swag-
gered around the Donelson station.

"He's a cad," she told Robert Hays, her husband, as they
rode home together following a family dinner at her
mother's, "just a badly mannered, conceited cad. I declare, I
don't see how Rachel puts up with him."

Captain Hays was a gentle, soft-spoken man. He leaned
from his saddle to pat his wife's sleeve. "I reckon Rachel says
the same thing about you and me," he teased, chuckling,
and when to punish him, Jane spurred her horse to a gallop,
he could only follow, still smiling at his pretty wife's loyalty.

Rachel meanwhile was caught between the memory of the
romantic young Virginian she believed she had married and
the overbearing autocrat who was in fact her husband. Dis-
mayed, she heard him speak sharply to one of Catherine's
little girls then turn on her, Rachel, with a torrent of sar-
casm when she remonstrated; she resented his patronizing
manner to her mother and held her breath lest Samuel or one
of the other brothers notice and call him to account. Yet
Lewis could be entirely engaging when he chose to be and
he was in one of his gayest moods when, not long after his
arrival, accompanied by John Overton, they rode out to look
at their land. The tract was known as *Clover Bottom,* and it
was well named, green, fertile, clover-carpeted.

They planned where the house should be built, where the
cotton and tobacco should be planted, where the orchard
should stand. Work could begin at once. They were laugh-

ing, chatting, riding three abreast across a cleared upland
on their way home, when Lewis suddenly leaned across
Rachel to address Overton who rode on her other side.

"By the way, that hobbledehoy at the house, that fellow
Jackson — he couldn't possibly be the interesting Andrew
Jackson you once told me about, could he?" Robard's voice
was weighted with contempt.

Overton, watching the treacherous rise and dip of the land
over which they were traveling, did not turn as he answered,
but his face darkened. "Well," he said slowly, "the man at
Mrs. Donelson's is Andy Jackson and he does happen to
be the man I told you about the last time I stopped in Harrodsburg. But I'd not call him a hobbledehoy. He's my
friend and law partner, Lew, just in case that fact has escaped you."

Robards gathered his bridle reins to form a thong and
brought it down savagely across his horse's neck, then pulled
the plunging animal to a slow trot beside the other two
horses while the thong came down again and again on the
straining neck. Rachel closed her eyes against the sight of
the senseless brutality. John continued to look straight ahead.

"No, the fact hadn't escaped me," Lewis retorted, "but one
wonders when your esteemed partner does his share of the
partnership's business. He's so forever under foot. I never
leave the house that he isn't coming in, and I never cross
the enclosure to the house that he isn't coming out. Of a
truth, the fellow makes himself at home, doesn't he?"

Rachel's indignation had been mounting but she had

kept silent, determined not to be drawn into a quarrel. But now the words of defense sprang from her lips in spite of her best efforts.

"We hope Mr. Jackson does feel at home — just as you and John do," she said. "As for his coming and going, we see him seldom except at mealtimes and not always then. Don't judge him harshly, Lewis. He's so eager to be friends."

"So I've noticed!"

Lewis spurred his horse to a killing pace over the uneven ground and when John and Rachel reached the Donelson station they found the animal, its head drooping, its sides heaving and dark with sweat, standing at the gate. Robards was nowhere in sight.

Rachel went directly to the house, John to his cabin. When supper time came, Jackson's chair was vacant, but he arrived while William was carving the roast, and after making his apologies to his hostess for being late, he smiled across the table at Rachel.

"Stockley was telling me this afternoon that you were going to select a spot for your new home today, Mrs. Robards. I hope you found it to your liking."

Rachel thought how boyishly interested he was, how at ease without being in the least presuming. "*Clover Bottom's* really lovely," she answered. " I hope we can have the house where we can see the river. . . ."

"We'll build it where it is practical, regardless of the view," Lewis interrupted casually as he helped himself to spoonbread, so casually, in fact, that Jackson scarcely heard him and continued turning alternately to him and to Rachel.

"When you're ready to build, do let me know, because I think I can get you some fine carpenters from up Salisbury way. Some boys up there have made a name for themselves, going to form a company, I reckon, and . . . ."

Robards laid down his fork and leaned across the table. "Mr. Jackson," he said, "when I want help of any kind in conducting my life or building my house I'll be pleased to let you know."

The silence that followed was briar-edged with discomfort for everyone. Samuel tried to break it by telling about an amusing foray he had had with a mother skunk and her two kittens that morning; Rachel made light of her own sense of direction so far as the river was concerned. But everyone was painfully aware of Robards's rudeness and the dinner finally broke up with each avoiding his neighbor's eyes.

The following morning Overton told Rachel that Jackson was moving to another station for the time being. It was a new humiliation for Rachel and her mother, though both saw the wisdom of the move. Rachel, determined to save her marriage at any cost, went quietly about her plans for the house at *Clover Bottom*. She rode into Nashville with Samuel and shopped at Clark's store for curtain chintz, bought candle molds and ticking and kitchen spoons. The moment the floors were laid and the fireplace ready for its first fire, she told herself, they would move in. Once alone with Lewis, she felt sure she could control his jealousy.

In the store, busy with her thoughts, fingering patterns of chintz, she did not see Samuel wave or hear his boyish, "Hi!" until suddenly Andrew Jackson loomed from the shadows among the bolts of cloth and jugs of molasses.

"How's the house coming, Mrs. Robards?" he asked with easy friendliness. He seemed not to notice her selfconsciousness, and while she told him about the progress Lewis's carpenters were making, he helped Samuel gather up her packages and then walked with them to the mounting block. When finally they rode away down the trail toward *Clover Bottom,* he stood for long minutes looking after them. "Rachel — " he said, and again, "Rachel."

Before the spring had advanced far, the Robards house was finished, the first planting was showing promise and Rachel made plans for the traditional housewarming. But here again Lewis declined to have any part of it. There would be no "backwoods roistering" in his house, he declared. So the idea was abandoned. Fall came, crops poorly cultivated, were not good, and in late October, after months of comparative quiet, Indians attacked *Clover Bottom.*

The attack came without warning, and as Lewis was sick in bed with a heavy cold at the time, Rachel rallied the field hands and was able to ward off the marauders without loss of life or serious damage to the plantation. But Robards was through with *Clover Bottom,* indeed through with the Cumberland. He was moved to Mrs. Donelson's stockade to convalesce at Christmas time when sullenly, quietly, he began making plans to return to Harrodsburg.

The Christmas of 1789 was marred for every member of the Donelson clan by Robards's glowering, and "Aunt Rachel" gave herself over with a will to keeping the children amused. They must not feel the tension that was making everyone else miserable. She roasted apples in the fireplace; she played Blind Man's Buff and Water, Water, Wine Flower; she told stories and sang songs until her throat ached. And because by common consent all callers remained away and there was no one but himself to praise or admire Rachel, Lewis admitted the Christmas had been "amusing."

In April, 1790, he started north with a friend named Thomas Crutcher. His good-bys both to Rachel and to Mrs. Donelson were casual and friendly, nothing more, and watching him ride away, Rachel asked herself bitterly whether she was wife, widow, or spinster.

Chapter 5

FUTILE JOURNEY

Andrew Jackson, hot-tempered, young, chivalrous, found much to occupy him these days. His practice was growing in leaps and bounds. Beside this, he was still riding the territory as Judge McNairy's public prosecutor and traveled to far places and for long periods of time.

The western part of North Carolina, that is the Cumberland, irked by various bunglings of the Congress, was demanding that it become a territory within the Federal Government. It wanted better mail service, better roads, more dependable protection against Indians. So the Cumberland received the unwieldly name of Territory-of-the-United-States-of-America- South-of-the-River-Ohio. Andrew Jackson formally took the oath of allegiance to the United States and was named Attorney of the District.

His duties were many, his days crowded, but beyond duty, above the press of the most intricate cases was the thought of the gentle, beautiful woman, Rachel Robards. For Jackson admitted to himself now that he loved her. A man of honor, he knew he must not by so much as a word or a look betray his love for she was the wife of another man.

Rachel herself was trying desperately to fill her days so full of thought for others that she would have no time to think of her own lot. She was busy at *Clover Bottom,* telling herself that it was still her home, even though she lived there alone with the cook for company and the field hands for protection.

It was several weeks after Robards's departure that word filtered back which answered all too clearly the question that had been plaguing Rachel ever since she had watched him ride away: when would he come back? He had told Thomas Crutcher that he hated everything about the Cumberland settlement and hoped he never would see it again.

Rachel felt suddenly free yet singularly trapped; free from continuous criticism and suspicion, trapped by the very freedom which robbed her of any definite status either in the community or within her own heart. To have been known in all pioneer forthrightness as "the Widow Robards" or as "Miss Donelson," her mother's one unmarried daughter, this might have given her the solid dignity she wanted. But to be the wife of a man who manifestly preferred living without her, this was a bitter cup to taste.

Still, Rachel was young, scarcely twenty-three, sunny natured, eager to join in the good times of the settlement whenever duties at *Clover Bottom* gave her the time. She was watching her fields, anxious for a good second harvest; she was teaching several young women slaves to sew neatly, to spin a smooth thread. So there was not much time left for merriment. However, no week passed without a day and often a night spent at her mother's stockade and another with Jane and Robert Hays. She saw Andrew Jackson seldom, for though he and John Overton were still using Overton's cabin for an office, he kept his room and had most of his meals at the Mansker station nearer Nashville.

One morning in early June as Rachel stepped through the doorway of her mother's house into the enclosure, she saw John coming toward her, in his hands a packet of letters and on his face a quizzical, half-questioning expression.

"For you — all of 'em," he said and put the packet into her hands.

She looked from the letters to his eyes which seemed to be focused on a butterfly somewhere above her head. Angered, disgusted at what he suspected was one of his kinsman's dramatic moves to call attention to himself, John could not bring himself to meet her bewildered gaze.

"John, you mean — you mean these are *all* from Lewis? Why, after almost two months of silence, should he suddenly write — look, there must be a dozen letters?"

"Lew is unpredictable, you know, but — if there is anything that bothers you in those" — he tapped the packet — "you'll let me know?" He still watched the butterfly lest his carefully guarded expression tell her too much.

"Thank you, John, I will," she said. She nodded and turned back into the house.

In her room she sank down on a low chest, the letters

spread out before her, and looked at their dates. Then she opened the first one. Half an hour later Rachel still sat re-reading the letters, now in their chronological order, now at random. Finally she gathered them up and put them into the small basket containing her over-night necessities. Then she went to the window and stood looking out across the en-closure to the forest beyond. Her breath came in gusts and she put her hands to her throat as though to ease the beating of the pulses there.

Robards had written that he was deeply ashamed of his behaviour, that he loved her, wanted her at his side. To-gether they could make a fresh start and, he added as a clinching argument, his mother whom she loved was ill and asked daily when she was coming. Would she not, if she cared at all, come to two people who needed her?

The letters were all of a piece, contrite, boyishly insistent, loving. He was her husband, he loved her, wanted her. There was no hesitation in Rachel's heart. Of course she would go to him. She was needed. That was enough for her generous nature.

Her mother was busy in the weaving room, so she hurried across the yard to Overton's cabin. Andrew Jackson she knew was with Judge McNairy somewhere on their circuit, so she burst in without her usual tap on the door.

"John," she spoke breathlessly, challengingly, "Lewis wants me to come to Harrodsburg. No matter what I may have said about never returning there, I'm going."

Overton looked up from the brief he was studying and

took off his glasses. "Oh?" was all he said.

"Yes, don't you think it's good, right that I should? Don't you think I owe our marriage this one more chance?"

He studied her a moment, then, "If I thought you could save it, yes, by all means. But, Rachel. . . ."

"I know what you're going to say, John. You're going to say Lewis will just begin the threats and criticisms all over again. But honestly, I don't think he will. On the other hand, if I don't go and he should return here, there might be another duel. Who knows? I keep telling myself it happened once and. . . ."

John got up and came around the table. Gently he took Rachel's hand in his. "You know, I think it's high time you heard the truth about something, Rachel," he said. "It won't be pleasant, but I think you'll be better for knowing."

"Why — why, what do you mean?"

"Just this. Here, sit down." With the toe of his boot he drew a chair forward and pushed her gently into it. "You spoke of 'another duel.' Rachel, that duel with Peyton Short — that duel was never fought."

For probably thirty seconds Rachel could not believe she had heard what her brain told her she had. She sat perfectly rigid, staring up at Overton, her hands clasped in her lap, her face white.

"*What?*" The exclamation burst from her in sickening disbelief. "But — but Lewis told me. . . ."

"Forget what he told you, Rachel. The morning I left Harrodsburg — you were there at the time — I asked Lew

about the duel. He told me the truth. I rode away in such a
fog of anger and shame and downright despair that I cannot even remember saying good-by."

As he spoke, Rachel was seeing again the little tab-
leau at the gate when John Overton, taking leave of Lewis
Robards, had mounted and wheeled his horse as though in
sudden disgust and had ridden away without a backward
glance or the customary wave of the hand.

"John, you—you mean Lewis challenged Peyton Short to a
duel because he felt Short had led me to betray our marriage, and then for some reason didn't — didn't go through
with it?"

"Short offered him a substitute, Rachel. He offered him
money — quite a large sum — one thousand dollars."

"*And Lewis accepted it?*" The words were scarcely
audible.

Overton nodded.

"Lewis — my husband — first accused me of being a wanton. Then he actually sold, yes, *sold* my honor and his — sold
it! Oh, John, John, what have I ever done to bring a thing
like this down upon my head? Not only mine but Mama's —
all the Donelsons'?"

"You haven't done anything, my dear. Unfortunately you
married a man whose whole nature has been dominated and
ruined by insane jealousy. Whatever of loftiness or fine feeling there may have been in that nature to begin with has
been so blunted by his own obsession that there isn't much
left. That's why I felt I must speak to you now before you

start back to join him. If you're determined to go, I want you to go with your eyes open. Lew is my cousin and it's not easy to say these things, but sometimes one has no choice."

Rachel got up. "Thank you for everything, John," she said slowly. "I must think this through." She gave his arm a friendly pat and stepped out into the sunshine.

Having "thought it through" however, Rachel still felt her place was with her husband since he had begged her to come to him. She waited until a party of pioneers was passing through in the direction of Harrodsburg and joined them. Her heart was heavy for she knew there could be no possible happiness for her in their reunion. Her respect for Robards was gone, but the memory of the man she had married five years earlier still persisted and there was always the hope in her heart that a miracle might restore that gallant, chivalrous gentleman to her. At least he had humbled himself in the writing of many letters imploring her to give him one more chance.

However, Rachel had been in Harrodsburg less than an hour when she realized how futile had been her hopes. Lewis greeted her with a characteristic tirade.

"You didn't hurry, did you?" he sneered. "With such attractions in Nashville I'm not surprised. A pity you came at all."

Before the astonished Rachel could fully grasp what he meant, Robards had flung himself out of the room and a moment later she heard the clatter of his horse's galloping hoofs as he raced toward the town.

It was her mother-in-law, bed-ridden now but mentally as alert as ever, who took Rachel in her arms. "My child, my dear, dear child," the sick woman comforted her, holding the dark head against her breast, "no one knows how glad I am to see you — or what I would give if you had not come!"

Rachel sat up, looking into the great eyes searching her own. "You wish I hadn't come, Mother? Why?" A strand of white hair, escaped from the frilled nightcap, straggled across the old woman's forehead and Rachel tenderly, almost absently, tucked it back as she spoke.

"Because, dear, this is no place for you. I learned only this morning that Lewis was expecting you — that he had written you. If I had known and if I had been strong enough, I should have sent you word not to come."

"But. . . .?"

"Lewis will never be a husband to you again — that I know. Bitterness has warped his very reason. His asking you to come here was just one more wild, illogical way he had of telling himself that he could force you if he chose. Oh, I know my boy so well! Go back, Rachel, go back, child. Lewis is drinking far more than he should. It isn't safe for you here."

"But you, dear?"

"I shall make out very well for the short time that is left me. My servants are loyal. My whole concern is for you. Send a note to your people by one of my Negro boys who knows the way and will lose no time. Meanwhile, my dressing room is yours. I shall want your constant attention."

So, thanks to the courageous conspiracy, Rachel saw very little of her husband who seldom came to the sickroom. When he did, his attitude was that of a lovingly tolerant husband who generously permits his wife to give her time exclusively to his sick mother.

Rachel took deep pleasure in waiting on the little old lady whom she always had loved. She never tired of making new delicacies, of reading aloud or softly singing the half-forgotten songs the invalid loved to hear. Meanwhile she watched the road and kept her bag packed. She was two hundred miles from Nashville, and every pasing hour was an added hazard. And then late one afternoon she saw a horseman turn in the lane. It was Andrew Jackson.

Years later Rachel would look back on that summer twilight and marvel at her own calm. She went to the sickroom, cupped the patient little white race lovingly in her two hands and said quietly, "Darling, they've come for me, so I'm going now. Yes, my bag's packed, my bonnet's out. Good-by — and bless you." A quick kiss lest the tears start, a final look around to make sure the bell was within reach, a wave from the doorway and she was running down the stairs to the verandah.

Even before she nodded a welcome to Jackson as he flung himself from the saddle, she had ordered her own horse saddled and brought around. Her heart thudded wildly as she explained her hurry to be off before Lewis should return from the errand that had taken him to Harrodsburg. "But you must be dreadfully tired, Mr. Jackson," she amended, seeing the dust white on his buckskin jacket and the lines of weariness in his face.

He smiled down at her. "No, only tired to death of knowing you are miserable, and being forced to stand by and do nothing about it. That's why I'm here."

He fastened her bag to the saddle, lifted her up, and with a quick, reassuring smile, re-mounted his own horse and led the way, cantering back in the direction from which he had come. Rachel's swift-footed mare kept abreast his big rangey bay and they soon had left Harrodsburg far behind.

Jackson explained how, when her note had been delivered, her brothers, her mother, and John Overton had held a conference. Samuel had seemed again the right one to bring her home as he had before. But Samuel was untried in dealing with men of Robards's unpredictable nature — for this time Robards might refuse to let Rachel go. Then John had volunteered to go, taking Stockley with him. However, he, Jackson, had returned to Nashville that day and had convinced the others that he was the logical one to go. He knew the country, every inch of it, so well; and he had no misgivings about being able to deal with Lewis Robards if necessary. As fate would have it, he had not been obliged to.

As they rode along, Rachel's spirits rose. A comforting sense of security replaced the nervous tension and panic of the past weeks. She was going home again, and with a man so thoughtful and kind that just being with him was guarantee enough that all was well with her world — and would continue to be.

They found shelter at night in settlers' cabins which Jackson located from memory, and before dawn they were on their way again, putting as much distance as possible between themselves and Robards's possible decision to follow and overtake them. And it was well they hurried along, for scarcely had Jackson deposited Rachel safely at her brother-in-law, Robert Hays's plantation, than Robards came dashing up.

His manner at first was conciliatory, even apologetic, as he tried to ingratiate himself again with the members of the Donelson family. However, when he realized the futility of his efforts, when in fact, Rachel told him frankly that she never would return to him, then Robards reverted to abuse. Finally his accusations became too slanderous and Captain Hays ordered him off the place.

"Tell Rachel I'll haunt her always," he shouted as he sprang into the saddle.

When he was gone, Rachel locked the door of her room and broke into tears. That she, Rachel Donelson, should have had a part in a domestic tragedy which had degenerated into a common farce!

Chapter 6

FLIGHT

ALL his life through Andrew Jackson detested the British. He had only to hear the word and his memory would travel back to the Waxhaws where his mother had been made a refugee and she and his brothers had died indirectly as a result of the war with Great Britain.

In Louisiana and Mississippi, Spanish territory, American settlers disliked Spain as cordially as Andrew Jackson did Great Britain. About thirty miles above Natchez on the Mississippi River stood *Springfield,* the magnificent estate of Colonel Thomas Green, an old friend of Colonel Donelson's. The Greens had invited Rachel often to come to them for a visit and if the journey had not been so dangerous she might have been tempted to accept their latest invitation shortly after she returned from Harrodsburg. Then, as though the visit were foreordained, something occured which made it imperative that she accept.

Autumn had come again. Color flamed in the forest, and in Rachel's cheeks as restored happiness gave her a zest for living. She busied herself about her mother's house, helping with the Thanksgiving preparations; then she was off to Jane's spacious home, *Haysboro,* to try some songs on the new harpsichord; again she forced herself to ride over to *Clover Bottom* which she was closing, to bring back the candle molds and polished wooden bowls bought with such bright hopes a year earlier.

Though Andrew Jackson still refused to live at the Donelson station, he was often there with John Overton. Besides, Stockley Donelson was interested in law and Jackson frequently had supper and spent the evening talking with him before the fire in the big common room. Unconsciously Rachel felt a sense of lack, of vague disappointment when she took her place at the long table and did not see Jackson's shock of tawny hair and saber-scarred face at the other end. Stability, forthrightness, these were the characteristics she had come to associate with him, and underlying them all a tenderness that was the more incredible because of the fiery temper that was its counterpart.

One evening shortly before Christmas, 1790, John Overton and Jackson, together with Robert Hays and his wife and Stockley Donelson, all had supped with Mrs. Donelson and Rachel. A heavy, wet snow was falling and Jane and Robert left early, then Overton and Jackson plodded across the compound to the cabin. Only Stockley remained, sitting in front of the fire, on his usually smiling face a look of deep concern. Rachel took the settle across from him and picked up her knitting, watching him furtively. Stockley was not himself this evening.

Finally, when she could not stand the uncertainty any longer, "What is bothering you, Stockley?" she asked. "I hope you and Mr. Jackson haven't had a disagreement?"

Stockley shifted in his chair, shook his head indecisively, then burst out, "Rachel, I — I haven't wanted to spoil things again just when you're beginning to be happy, but. . . ."

"But what, brother?"

He took a deep breath. "Today a man came through from Harrodsburg. . . ." Rachel caught her breath. "Go on!"

"He said Lew Robards is boasting all over Harrodsburg that, come spring when the snow's gone from the mountain roads, he's getting a posse of men and he's coming down here to carry you back. He's telling everyone we took you from him by force."

"Stockley, tell me, who else knows? Does Mama? Or John Overton? Or Mr. Jackson?"

"No, not anybody. I wanted to see whether I couldn't think of something to do before I spoke to *anyone*, even you. And I think mayhap I have thought of something."

"Go on." Rachel realized with an odd little shock that her voice, though she thought she spoke normally, was only a whisper.

"Well, this morning I met Colonel Stark at the tavern. He's taking his flatboat to Natchez along about the first of the year. Mrs. Stark's going with him. . . ."

"And so am I!"

"I thought something like that, except the trip's so dangerous. It's Indian country all the way and Stark's not taking any militiamen, thinks he and his crew can handle any situation."

"Nevertheless, Stockley, I'm going. I'm going down to *Springfield* to be with the Greens. They've coaxed and coaxed, and now I'm going. The journey can't be any more dangerous than the one we all took aboard the old *Adventure* when we were children. Besides, I'd rather face Indians than run the risk of another single day in Harrodsburg."

"I'd give a pretty if Andrew Jackson were going! You know, Rachel, I've more faith in him when it comes to Indians than a whole company of militia." Stockley got to his feet and stood staring into the fire. "As a matter of fact," he added slowly, "I've more faith in him no matter *what* the circumstances, than any man I know."

There was a long silence punctuated only by the hiss of sap in some green logs on the fire and by the click of Rachel's flying needles. It was she who broke it. "I have, too," she said. Then, after a pause, "But Mr. Jackson's so busy. Only the other day he was telling me the number of cases he has coming up within the next few months. We'll work out some way for me to go with the Starks, never doubt it. I'll tell Mama in the morning and we'll plan my clothes. Oh, I'm so glad you told me quickly, so glad you thought of Colonel Stark! The part of my life that included Lewis is definitely closed and nothing is going to re-open it! I realize now that he is the only person I ever have really been afraid of — and I am afraid of him, terribly afraid."

"Sister," Stockley leaned over, meticulously selected a small log from the pile stacked against the face of the fireplace, and laid it on the fire, "have you ever thought of divorcing Lew?"

Rachel's needles clicked faster. "I can't imagine thinking of it — of any Donelson woman thinking of it. But even though I did, you know, Stockley, that it would be impossible."

"Why?"

"Simply because our laws don't recognize a woman's right to ask for a divorce. Even John Overton admits that. I heard him discussing it the other day with Samuel. Some day there may be new laws, but there aren't any now. John was telling Samuel that most of our laws are taken from the English laws, and you know you never heard of an English woman asking for a divorce from her husband. It just isn't done. I can't imagine it myself."

"Well, then, how about the Spanish territory around New Orleans or Natchez?"

"Honestly, I don't know." Rachel shrugged her shoulders and bent to pick up a stitch she had dropped, smoothing the stocking across her lap. "Don't let's talk about it any more — it's something I don't like."

As a subject of interest Christmas took second place in the Donelson family that year. Mrs. Donelson, between tears and laughter, helped Rachel pack her boxes; Jane, trying to hide her own misgivings, dwelt on what she had heard about the

romantic elegance of life along the Mississippi in the Deep
South. William, Alexander, and Samuel were belligerent and
thought Robards might be permanently cured of his high-
handed audacity if they met him and his "posse" and proved
to them once and for all that the Donelson men were not to
be trifled with. Stockley, who in this one instance felt responsible for Rachel's decision to make the journey, gave a
great sigh of relief.

Andrew Jackson, when he heard of the proposed voyage,
spoke his mind. He had property not far from Natchez
which needed some attention. To send Mrs. Robards off in
the care of the Starks and the crew of their boat was, in his
estimation, unthinkable. Colonel Stark might be an excellent
navigator and a thoroughly worthy man, but he was no
leader. He, Jackson, would consider it an honor if the Donelsons would entrust Mrs. Robards to his care. Thus his offer
was phrased in all its formal, old time punctiliousness. Thus
once more did Rachel Donelson and Andrew Jackson set
out upon a hazardous journey.

In her heart Rachel must have known the truth: that Andrew Jackson loved her. And that knowledge must have
made her dark eyes sparkle and her laughter echo among
the musty timbers of Colonel Stark's flatboat on the bleak
morning early in 1791 when it drew away from its moorings
and lumbered out into mid-stream.

Wrapped in a cape of heavy wine-colored wool, its hood
drawn over her hair, she leaned against the bulwark of the
cabin, waving to the little group on the shore. There was
Stockley waving his hat — William squinting into the cold off

the river —John Overton now and again lifting his hand in a
salute then turning again to Samuel with whom he seemed
to be in deep conversation. And Samuel, the best loved,
Samuel seemed not to take his eyes from the boat. Farther
away, dimmer, now the settlement itself shrunken to a mere
cluster of shadows, and then only the river and the forest.

Rachel stifled a sigh and turned to find the cubicle she was
to share with Mrs. Stark, turned and found herself looking
into Andrew Jackson's eyes. The boat swayed slightly and he
steadied her with a hand on her elbow. His eyes were smiling, his voice warm but impersonal when he said, "Try to
enjoy this journey, Mrs. Robards. Try to rest. I make no
doubt it's been a long time since you've been free from re-
sponsibility, so now that you are free, take advantage of
your leisure. The Starks are kindly people, so don't hesitate
to call on Mrs. Stark for anything you may need. And you
know I am always at your service."

She looked up at the scarred, bony face and suddenly her
eyes filled. How good he was — how kind! She managed a
fleeting smile, touched his sleeve, then, lest he see her brimming eyes, she hurried inside.

A month passed as the boat made its perilous way along
the Cumberland into the Ohio and so on to the Mississippi.
Gradually the scenery changed from the rugged to the softly
semi-tropical. The hills drew back, the moss-draped forests
leaned closer. And in and out among the shadows, now seen,
now only suspected, slipped the lithe, copper-hued enemy.
There were no major attacks but more than one arrow im-
bedded itself in the boat's timbers.

Rachel saw Andrew Jackson almost constantly, yet paradoxically she seldom saw him to speak to alone. He spent his time with the Colonel and the crew while Rachel helped Mrs. Stark with the housekeeping and the cooking. Sometimes her heart misgave her. Did Andrew Jackson suspect the place he had come to hold in her life? Again, she wondered, were all his kindnesses in the face of so much inconvenience, so much danger, simply evidence of his chivalry? Or did her welfare really mean so much to him that he gladly risked his practice, his reputation, his life, to stand between her and whatever danger might befall? She wondered, and one day when they had almost reached their journey's end, Rachel had her answer.

The boat was idling along through what had become nothing more than an alley curving in and out of the forest. The sun had set and mist like steam rising from a giant cauldron, floated before and behind the boat, shutting it in, a little segment of moving life in a world of utter silence.

Rachel sat in the little curtained-off part of the cabin which she shared with Mrs. Stark, idly watching the shore slip by. Lanterns were seldom lighted and she knew daylight would not last long enough to enable her to mend the rip in her skirt. She tapped her thimble against her lips, dreaming, gazing into space. And then she saw the canoe slide into the water and head for the flatboat! Behind it came another and still another, each manned by three naked savages, silently, like something seen in a nightmare.

Rachel dropped her sewing and ran out into the cabin where Colonel Stark sat working over his log while his wife sat beside him knitting in the dim candlelight. "Indians, Colonel Stark!" Rachel cried. "Where is Mr. Jackson? I just saw them, nine of them, and there may be more — I didn't wait to see."

She ran up the companionway followed by the Colonel. Jackson stood in the bow, watching the shoreline. He turned at Rachel's urgent call and as he did, the first brown arm came stealthily up over the side and from some unseen vantage point an arrow fell where he had stood an instant before. Rachel ran back to the cabin for the musket beside her bunk and came out on deck again in time to see both the Colonel and Jackson firing. The brown arm had disappeared but another and then another arrow came zinging to a frustrated stop in the deck floorboards.

Jackson and the Colonel stood just outside the companionway where they had an unbroken view of both sides of the boat; the three men who comprised the crew, all seasoned marksmen, covered the stern. As yet no one aboard had been wounded and the yells of pain coming from the water indicated that shots from the boat had found their marks.

Rachel took her place between Jackson and Colonel Stark, her musket resting on her arm, her face alight with eagerness. Her father had taught her to shoot as he had to ride and had been well pleased with her marksmanship. She and Samuel had spent hours with bow and arrow, shooting at a target, and her aim with a musket was excellent.

"If only one could see through this fog," she murmured, shifting her position.

For the first time Andrew Jackson realized that she had

come up on deck again and was standing beside him. For an instant he took his eyes from the dusk-shrouded river and looked at her with frank consternation.

"Mrs. Robards, please," he exclaimed, his eyes again focusing on the side of the boat, "please, I must insist that you go below. I think we've beaten off that little raiding party, but there's no telling; there may be a hundred of them ashore right now just waiting for the dark . . . .".

"But I'm not in the least afraid, Mr. Jackson, really I'm not." Rachel was leaning backward in her earnestness, her brow puckered, as she looked up at him towering above her. "Why may n't I stay and help? I'm a good shot."

Colonel Stark had maneuvered his way around the corner of the cabin, hoping for a better view. So quickly that Rachel could not believe it was happening, Jackson put his arm about her shoulder and drew her to him. "I want you to go below," he said, "because your safety means more to me than anything on earth — Rachel. Now go." For an instant their eyes met and held. Then he gently turned her toward the companionway.

Back in her cubicle, she sank down on her bunk and put her palms against her cheeks which were suddenly flaming. Rachel had her answer.

Chapter 7

NATCHEZ

Springfield, with its white pillars, gleaming silver and crystal, its ancient mahogany and satinwood, was a bit of Virginia set down in the tropical green of Mississippi. Luxury, gaiety, all the things farthest removed from the stark pioneer life of the Cumberland, these filled the days at *Springfield.*

Rachel forgot her first shyness in the friendly atmosphere of the plantation and was soon the center of a lively group of young people who danced and rode and picnicked through the late winter months. In her heart she held a secret that brought a new glow to her eyes and cheeks and a provocative curve to her lips. Rachel never had been so beautiful.

What if "Mr. Jackson" in an excess of prudence, did withdraw into a quiet shell of conservatism? The words he had spoken so impulsively the evening of the Indian raid aboard

the flatboat were burned indelibly into her consciousness.
He had called her Rachel. The memory of his voice when
he had spoken the name was a song in her heart.

She refused to admit to herself how very slight were the
chances that she ever could be more than that — Rachel —
to Andrew Jackson. She only knew she felt safe, cared for,
for the first time in years, and for the present that must be
enough. She would not think of the future.

Jackson did not remain long at *Springfield* though the
Greens were determined he should. He was anxious to see
to his property on Bayou Pierre before returning to Nashville
for the April court session. He took with him into the bayou
country just one man, Jason, a trusted Negro who was
thoroughly familiar with the twisting, moss-shrouded waterways; and early one morning Rachel saw his canoe slip away
from the *Springfield* landing.

Drifting through the shadowy world of green foliage re-
flected in greener water, Jackson tried to take stock of himself and of his love for Rachel. Sooner or later Mississippi
would take up arms against the Spanish who were encroach-
ing upon its territory above the 31st parallel which was the
recognized southern boundary of the United States. Should
he persuade the woman he loved to obtain a divorce under
the Spanish law in Mississippi? Such a divorce would be
easily obtained.

They could then be married and settle at Bayou Pierre.
There he could have a paying plantation and at the same

time indulge his one hobby: breeding and racing thoroughbred horses. From boyhood horses had been one of his great
interests; now he was a man grown, with a woman he loved
to share the years ahead. Why not give up law? Because he
was ambitious for the best things in life as his mother had
been before him, he believed that law as a profession was
an excellent springboard to almost any position in the affairs
of the growing nation. From choice, however, he would have
taken plantation life. Then why not give up law and be a
planter in Mississippi?

Through the gold flecked green of the bayou he could
see his spacious plantation house, could see his beautiful
wife, his Rachel, moving through its rooms. He could see
his fine stables, his pastures dotted with brood mares and
their long legged colts. He and Rachel, hand in hand, walked
across the lawn sweeping down to the bayou — Rachel love-
lier as time passed. But . . . .

Jackson started and an exclamation of impatience sprang
to his lips.

Jason turned. "Anything wrong, suh? See a moccasin?"

"No, Jason, no moccasin. I just remembered something I
shouldn't have forgotten."

"Does we go back and get it, suh?"

Jackson shook his head and when Jason's back was turned
again he smiled ruefully. How could he have let himself
dream so? How dared he, even in his thoughts, have sub-
jected Rachel to such danger? When Spanish claims to
Mississippi ended as they were sure to do within the next

decade, Spanish laws would be void. What then of a divorce granted under Spanish rule? He and Rachel would not be considered lawfully married and their children, should they have them, would be branded as illegitimate. No, that dream as a solution to their problem was as dangerous as it was childish.

For a day Jackson tramped over his property, then he was back at *Springfield*, subdued and taciturn, and packed his bags for the long trek north to the Cumberland. The evening before he was to leave, he walked out through one of the long windows opening on the gallery and saw Rachel coming up the broad steps from the garden. Some things are so natural, so spontaneous, that they seem part of a prearranged pattern. So it seemed entirely right that he should take her arm and turn her about and lead her back down into the jasmine scented garden.

There he drew her to him, his hand brushing back her dark curls, his lips against her temple. "Rachel — my darling — " the words were a whisper — "I could not leave you without saying I love you — I shall always love you."

Her fingers came up to touch his cheeks, to trace the deep scar across his brow and the bridge of his nose. "And I love you, too, Andrew — forever and ever. But —" she drew back in the circle of his arms — "what are we to do? What possible chance have we of — happiness — ever?"

In the silence the crickets chirred and down in the slave quarters a child wept sleepily, monotonously. Andrew tilted Rachel's face up, cupping it with both hands. There was no moon but the sky was aglitter with stars and in their light her face shone white, her eyes still, dark pools.

"My darling," he said, "just what chances we may have I don't know. At present we are helpless, but I have faith. No love so right as ours can possibly have been given us for nothing. As to what we can do — we can pray for some solution. But *whatever* the future may hold for us, I shall always be there, near you, waiting — if need be, to the end of my life and beyond."

He drew her close again, his cheek against hers. Tears choked her and she could only cling to him, whispering, "Andrew — Andrew — Andrew, my dear, my dear!"

Before dawn the next morning she watched from behind her shutters as he rode down the long avenue of trees and through the gates. He would travel overland, along the Chickasaw Trace through five hundred miles of Indian country dominated by the Choctaw and Chickasaw nations. It would be a perilous journey and a lonely one unless he joined a party somewhere along the way.

Rachel was too thoroughly imbued with the sturdy faith and optimism of all pioneer women to give herself up to pointless anxiety for the man she loved. Instead, she cherished the memories she had of their few moments together and looked confidently toward their reunion. Where or when that might be she did not question.

The languorous summer days came and the bayou country drowsed in the steaming heat. July, August, were gone and then one evening Rachel looked up from the length of tat-

ting in her lap to see Andrew Jackson crossing the lawn
deep in conversation with Colonel Green. They came on
together but at the gallery steps the Colonel turned aside
to the garden and Andrew hurried up alone.

Rachel ran to meet him, anxiety giving wings to her feet.
For he was not smiling and there were lines of — was it
weariness? discouragement? — running from nostril to mouth
corner. What had happened? Her mother? Jane? And then
she was in his arms and he was holding her, murmuring,
"Rachel, Rachel, my dear one!"

"Andrew — what is it? What has happened? Tell me!"

He smiled down at her, trying with all the tact at his
command to soften the blow he knew he must deal and at
the same time manage to convey his own deep gratitude
for the door it unlocked. "Rachel," he said quietly, "we have
what we prayed for, but it's not come as we'd have had it.
You're free."

"Free? What do you mean, Andrew? Has — has anything
happened to Lewis?"

"No, to the best of my knowledge he's in the best of health.
Lewis has divorced you."

"*Lewis* — divorced — *me*?" For a moment the full impact
of what she was hearing did not penetrate Rachel's brain.
Then the ugly truth struck. Jackson held her hands in his
own warm clasp while he explained what had happened.

Robards evidently had wanted to free himself from his
marriage so he persuaded a relative to introduce a bill in
the Virginia legislature making his application for divorce

legal. Rachel was accused of having "eloped" from her Harrodsburg home with Andrew Jackson. The legislature passed
the bill. John Overton had gone to Harrodsburg to make
sure everything was in order and had returned to say Rachel
was now free to re-marry.

"How *could* Lewis bring such a charge?" she cried. "He
knew it was not true — he knew his own mother urged me to
go and that my mother and brothers sent you for me. How
dared he perjure himself so?"

Yet Lewis, in spite of his claims to gentle breeding, his
chivalrous regard for all womanhood, had done just that.
Deliberately he had dealt Rachel a blow from which she
was never to recover. Joy there might be, but the undeserved
sense of guilt and shame would remain, never to be forgotten. Her complete innocence made the ugly accusation all
the more trying, and but for Andrew's unswerving devotion
and tenderness, it could not have been borne. It was Andrew
who reminded her that, no matter how low Robards might
have fallen, he nevertheless had released her and she was
free. A chapter was forever closed, the unhappy days were
gone.

Andrew Jackson and Rachel Robards were married in the
drawing room at *Springfield* in the early autumn of 1791 and
went to Bayou Pierre on their honeymoon. There, in the
peace and quiet, feeling for the first time that they had a
right to be together, Rachel relaxed. Together they walked
across the land and Andrew happily confessed his day-dream
of months past; together they visualized the mansion which

one day would replace the honeymoon cabin; but together they admitted they were homesick for the Cumberland!

They returned over the long Chickasaw Trace with a large party traveling north, and here Rachel had every opportunity of watching her husband's leadership in operation. One evening word reached them that Indians planned to attack just before the next dawn. Hugh McGary, another member of the party who was noted for his successful strategy in dealing with Indians, wanted the camp to sit tight and defend itself when the attack should occur. Jackson, who felt sure they were heavily outnumbered, proposed another course. He suggested that the camp fires be left burning, since there was no wind, and that the travelers be quietly on their way before midnight. His plan was followed and several hours later when the Indians came creeping into the camp they found it deserted. It was said that McGary never forgave Jackson for his superior strategy.

Never was a home coming more wholeheartedly joyous. Here was the beloved "little sister" whose lot had been so checkered with misery, safe at last and gloriously happy with a husband whom the whole family loved. Autumn was upon them so better judgement dictated they remain at Mrs. Donelson's station until spring when they would look for a house of their own.

Meanwhile Andrew and John Overton opened their new law office on the public square in Nashville. Both men were held in highest esteem for their integrity and legal experience, and as the stream of immigrants pouring into the

Cumberland was growing daily, their practice grew apace as land titles and claims were duly examined and evaluated. Sitting sewing or quietly reading beside her husband as he worked through the long winter evenings, Rachel knew that at last she understood what was meant by perfect happiness.

To a mind as keen as Andrew Jackson's, every journey his profession required of him sent him back home with a challenge, either legal or patriotic, to be met. The Federal Government continued to be — or seemed to be — stubbornly indifferent to the plight of the settlers in the Western District. During 1792-93 the powerful Cherokee Chief, Dragging Canoe, rallied the southern tribes and hoped, by forming a federation with the northwest Indians, to push back the entire western frontier. Though Dragging Canoe died, his young braves did their utmost to carry out his prophesy that the Western District — and this included the Cumberland — would become "a dark and bloody ground."

The territory around Nashville came in for its share of terror and as Andrew and John Overton were constantly on the move through Indian country, Rachel never sent her husband away without a fervent prayer for his safe return. Fear stalked the land. Buchanan's station, about four miles from Nashville, was attacked in September, 1792, and there followed one of the most dramatic Indian battles in American history.

Runners brought word of the battle to the Donelson station and Mrs. Donelson turned cold with fear for her friend Sally Buchanan. Sally, it was said, rallied the women inside the stockade to making bullets, loading guns, keeping a supply of drinking water within reach of the men who were defending the station. The fort withstood the attack, to be sure, but who could tell where or when another siege just as relentless would begin?

Shortly afterward, Andrew Jackson on one of his journeys, stopped at a station known as Henry's Station, in the same general location. He and a Lieutenant Telford had walked out a short distance from the station to look at the land, when suddenly a party of Indians, about three hundred, swooped down upon the station. The two men tried to get back and found themselves surrounded. Jackson managed to fight his way through but Telford was tortured and killed.

Jackson returned from that engagement more than ever bitter at the shilly-shallying methods of the Congress in dealing with the Indians. His anger over Telford's death, so fresh in his mind, brought him close to a break with John Overton. John, whose gentle nature tempered indignation with justice, reminded his friend of the many treaties with the Indians which the white settlers had chosen to ignore. How, he argued, could a savage defend his rights except by the only means he understood: brutality?

"Brutality," Jackson shouted, his temper blazing now, "brutality, yes, aided and abetted by the British! How dare you make excuse for them, John, when you think of the slaughter of innocent women and children?"

"I don't excuse them, Andy," the little man answered quietly. "No one hates all this torturing and killing more than

I do. I only say that *any* man will defend what he believes is his. That's what the War of Independence was all about — remember? Again and again we've promised the Indians to respect certain boundaries. But have we? You know the answer as well as I do: we haven't. We're the aggressor on his land — the Indian's — exactly as we feel England is on ours. So he wages war against us. Mind you, Andy, I despise Great Britain's part in it as much as you do, but . . . ."

"There's not a single 'but' about it, John," Jackson retorted. "I'll bid you good-night."

The conversation had occured one evening as Rachel, Andrew, and John sat late, talking, after the other members of the household had gone to bed. Andrew lit his candle at the hearth and stomped upstairs. Rachel shook her head and smiled at John.

"Great Britain and Indian warfare are two subjects Andrew bruises and bangs himself against the way an unbroken colt will against a bit. He'll apologize in the morning." And, of course, he did.

Andrew Jackson's heart was full of gratitude that winter and early spring for good fortune seemed suddenly to have selected him for special attentions. He was elected a trustee of Davidson Academy whose head was the Reverend Thomas B. Craighead and another of whose trustees was the great Revolutionary War hero, General Daniel Smith, second-in-command under Governor Blount of the territory. Then, he had found exactly the home place he wanted for himself and Rachel. It was a comfortable cabin of several

rooms and a lean-to, standing on a six hundred-and-thirty
acre tract of land just across the river from the Donelson
station. John Donelson had built it for his bride several years
earlier; now John, the restless one of the Donelsons, was
ready to move on to a new district.

It was May when Rachel and Andrew moved into their
scrubbed and shining cabin. Standing in the middle of its
common room, taking in the pretty curtains, the copper jugs
filled with spring flowers, the gay rugs Rachel and her sisters
had braided all through the winter months, they could only
smile into each other's eyes in deep content.

"Our very own home," Rachel breathed. "Nothing mean
or unworthy or ugly shall ever pass its door." She pressed
her cheek against Andrew's arm, her fingers twined about
his.

"Only your mean, unworthy, ugly husband," he teased,
and when she protested, he caught her around the waist,
lifted her and swung her in a circle until she shrieked in
helpless laughter to be put down.

So happy they were, so blissfully unprepared when the
blow fell.

Word came through that Lewis Robards never had been
granted a divorce but only *the right to file a petition for one*
with the Virginia Legislature. He never had filed the petition. Now he was re-marrying and had filed it and had been
granted a divorce.

When Andrew brought her the incredible news, Rachel
was aware of a quick stabbing pain in her heart, and then

her world turned black. When next she opened her eyes and found Andrew bending over her, his own face ashen, she knew she had not dreamed the horror. It was true; during their two years together she and Andrew had not been legally husband and wife.

Futile now to cry as she had earlier, "How could he have done such a thing?" Then at least she had believed the break to be a clean one; now, either wilfully or through ignorance, Robards had made her a social outcast and her marriage a farce. As to how such a thing could have happened with both Jackson and Overton lawyers, the only possible answer was (and is) that divorce was virtually unknown on the American frontier and it was natural enough to mistake the *right to file* a petition for the actual filing of the petition itself. Added to that was old Mrs. Robards's sincerity when she told Overton how she rejoiced with Rachel in her freedom, and all the word of mouth assurances along the trails and waterways that Lewis Robards had divorced his wife Rachel.

Bitterly Jackson blamed himself. There was no excuse, he insisted; he had been careless, had taken too much for granted. But Rachel, with the courage and the loving kindness which were her two strongest characteristics, comforted him. What was done was done, she said, once the first shock had abated. They were innocent of any wrong doing now as they had been two years earlier. Lewis had been either unpardonably cruel or incredibly stupid.

Rachel and Andrew Jackson were quietly re-married early

in 1794. They were both twenty-seven now but tragedy which had struck at them twice had given them a maturity far beyond their years. Rachel busied herself with her growing circle of young nieces and nephews and usually had several of them at *Poplar Grove,* the new home place. Andrew, a great admirer of General John Sevier, one of the greatest Indian fighters in American history, followed his example by carrying war into the Indian country instead of waiting for them to bring it to his. So, as Indian outrages continued, Andrew Jackson and a company of men from the Cumberland under the command of Major James Ore, marched to the Lower Towns of the Cherokees and once and for all time put a stop to the marauding expeditions.

It was a time of gravest anxiety for Rachel but she felt her lot was in no way different from that of the other women in the neighborhood. So she forced herself to sing at her work and to smile as she planned charades for the children. And at last the fighters were back, victorious; the Indian peril was definitely ended and Rachel Jackson could walk among the petunias and phlox in her garden without keeping one eye on the corn field for lurking warriors.

Chapter 8

HUNTER'S HILL

While Rachel was richly content in her home and her husband, asking nothing more than a continuation of their life together as they were now living it, Andrew was taking a somewhat more ambitious view.

"You're going to have the finest home in the Cumberland," he promised her.

"But what more could we wish for than *Poplar Grove?*" she insisted, looking about at its simplicity and loving it.

"Much, *much* more, Mrs. Jackson. Just you wait and see!"

So Andrew set out in the spring of 1795, bound for Philadelphia where he expected to dispose of about fifty thousand acres of land which he and John Overton owned jointly. With the money from the sale he planned to open a store near *Poplar Grove*. The constantly growing population needed just such a store. But the entire undertaking was a failure which brought Jackson and Overton close to financial ruin. In Philadelphia there were no buyers for southern land. Then a speculator, one David Allison, not only offered to buy the land but introduced Jackson to the heads of several wholesale houses and gave his notes for the merchandise ordered.

Not until several months later, with the goods delivered at high rates and the empty shelves of the new store ready to be filled, was it learned that Allison had defaulted on his notes. Andrew was faced with the problem of making good the payments that were due. It meant selling the store before actually it was opened; and this he did.

His absence had been a long one and during it Rachel had managed the farm at *Poplar Grove*. In heavy boots, a large straw hat shading her face, she had walked across their fields, loving the feel of the good warm earth against her soles; taking pride in their neat cabins; loving the loyal, friendly workers who cultivated the crops, picked the cotton, chopped and stacked the cord wood against the autumn's first chill. Home — the very sound was music. What need for more? And when Andrew's Philadelphia venture proved disastrous, his working capital gone, Rachel had only sympathy. Standing beside him in their doorway, pointing to their fields, she said, "While we have all this, dear, and each other, don't let's grieve too much over a loss of money. There'll be better times, I know."

In spite of reverses, the winter of 1795 was a happy one at *Poplar Grove*. Rachel took great pains to make guests feel welcome always and one such guest, an Easterner, after returning to his home, wrote a letter of appreciation which neither she nor Andrew ever forgot. After praising Rachel's charming hospitality, he added that he was going to propose Andrew's name as a representative in the Congress. The Jacksons, he said, were truly typical of the best in cultured American family life. At the same time Governor William Blount offered to put up Andrew's name for a Congressional seat. The two proposals coming almost simultaneously, seemed part of a plan, one of those strange, sudden fusions of recognition of a man's worth by several widely separated individuals at the same time.

No man with Andrew's keen mind, interested as he was in everything that affected the country he loved, could possibly remain unnoticed. Plans were finally taking shape to make a state of "The-Territory-South-of-the-River-Ohio." Jackson, from the beginning, had been one of the leading spirits in the plan and was chosen one of the men to represent Davidson County at Knoxville on the 11th of January, 1796, when the new state received its constitution.

As for its name? How characteristic was Jackson's speech before the Convention, edged as it was with his dislike of everything British: ". . . Since Independence there is no reason for copying anything from England. We should adopt for our new state the Indian name of the Great Crooked River, Tennessee, a word that has as sweet a flavor on the tongue as hot corn cakes and honey." Yes, Andrew Jackson was becoming a figure in the affairs of his state.

One day when he and Rachel were picnicking on a beautiful spot above a sweep of river and valley and she had cried out in wonder at the grandeur spread out before her, he made a confession. Their new house would stand on the exact spot they now occupied, this would be their view in the future. He had bought the land — *Hunter's Hill* it was called — and there Rachel should have the imposing home he always had dreamed he would build for her.

He was so boyishly jubilant, so sure of her delight, and she knew she must not disappoint him. But how could she tell him she was enchanted when the very thought of leaving *Poplar Grove* filled her with dismay? If her voice was a little shrill and her smile fixed, he did not notice.

"It will be a beautiful, *beautiful* house, Andrew," she repeated, realizing she had said it before, yet unable to think of a substitute. Then so spontaneously that the words surprised her as she uttered them, she asked, "But how can we afford such a pretentious place?"

Rachel might well ask. The Allison failure had drained their resources. Yet, within the next few years, so unquestioned was her husband's reputation for honorable dealing, he acquired vast tracts of land some of which he re-sold; he opened negotiations for several more stores, and he was elected to Congress. To Andrew Jackson a failure was a lesson learned, the better with which to build success.

The house at *Hunter's Hill* took shape quickly, a graceful, two-story frame structure with big, high-ceilinged rooms and windows looking out on one of the most magnificent views in the Cumberland. From Philadelphia came handsome car-

peting, drapes and furniture, and on Rachel's first lonely
Christmas there arrived a glittering little coach with her
monogram on its doors and a team of smart thoroughbreds
to carry her in it wherever her fancy dictated.

"The Jackson cabin," "the Jackson station," these had
passed and now "the Jackson place, *Hunter's Hill*," shining,
elegant, dominated the community. Its house servants and
field hands alike were well clothed, well fed and housed, its
rich black fields soon yielding bumper crops. And Rachel
knew that one day soon Andrew would have his own perfectly proportioned race course on which his own fine horses
would challenge the best racers in the country.

Rich fabrics, laces, gloves, delicate bottles of scent, these
all found their way to *Hunter's Hill*, to the beloved wife of
the man who in Philadelphia was becoming more and more
conscious of the urge toward public life.

Her own days were crowded. Through the entire region no
plea for help reached "Aunt Rachel's" ears that went un-
answered. Mounted on her sure-footed sorrel gelding, Nibs,
a bag of supplies lashed to the saddle, she was on her way.
Sometimes a man servant rode beside her, but more often
Rachel went alone.

Many a woman in agonizing pain looked up to see Rachel's
dark eyes smiling down on her and took fresh courage; many
a croupy child, gasping for breath, found that playing hid-
ing-from-the-Indians with "Aunt Rachel" under a steaming
blanket was great fun. breathed in the piny vapor from the
kettle she held — and lived. And when tragedy struck it was

"Aunt Rachel" who left her own snug hearth to bring comfort, to fold tired hands, to speak the beautiful: "Though I walk through the valley of the shadow of death I will fear no evil for Thou art with me. . . ."

Rachel's days were full, indeed, and equally so were her heart and her capable hands. The young girl who had eased the smart of small chapped knuckles aboard the *Adventure* had merely added years to her age and more healing unguents to her equipment.

Looking about her pretty bedroom on Christmas morning, Andrew's Christmas letter and his gifts on the table beside her, Rachel tried to be sensible. After all, this was but one Christmas. Andrew could not possible return from Philadelphia for the one day and then dash back; his letter had explained all that. Besides, he just had ben obliged to buy a new and expensive wardrobe, one better suited to a member of Congress. He would, he explained, be home as soon as posible and meanwhile he sent her all his love.

Rachel folded his letter and slipped it into her bodice and walked to the window. It had snowed in the night; now it had turned bitter cold and the world lay gray and still. On the driveway below she could see the tire and hoof marks made by her new coach and team which just had been driven around to the stable. She knew she was being childish and sentimental; Andrew's love wrapped her round like a warm cloak; success was bound to demand its price in absences, in adjustments of many kinds. Surely she was capable of accepting these with good grace.

Thus she berated herself, looking into the frozen hush of the valley. But in her own heart Rachel knew she was deliberately evading the one thing the thought of which brought the crimson to her cheeks and set her heart crashing so painfully as to make her breathless. Intangible yet not to be denied, uncertain as the sound of church bells in a gale, was the knowledge that in many places her very name was anathema. She was variously "that Mrs. Jackson," "that ill-bred, common woman," "that shameless creature married to such a distinguished man". . . . The list stretched out into the unpredictable future. Lewis had kept his promise to the letter: he *was* haunting her!

Her eyes filled but she brushed the tears away impatiently and turned from the window. She had invited the entire Donelson clan for Christmas dinner. Turkeys were roasting in the big ovens downstairs, yellow yams were sending up their own special pungency. Rachel hurried down. Given the opportunity she most loved, that of providing comfort of whatever kind to family, friends, guests, wayfarers, any who crossed her threshold, she began to glow with the lovely radiance that was such an integral part of her being. So away with self-pity.

The following year — 1797 — Andrew was appointed to succeed William Blount as United States Senator from Tennessee. Most of his time was given to arranging Indian treaties and to bringing before both houses the matter of back pay for men who had fought in the Indian wars. Then,

before the term had expired, he tendered his resignation
and was back at *Hunter's Hill,* looking after his plantation,
his law practice, his stores — he now owned stores in Gallatin,
Lebanon, at *Clover Bottom,* and at *Hunter's Hill* — and in
breeding and racing fine horses.

Public life, he discovered, was expensive and though one
side of his restless, ambitious nature responded to its call,
he wrote frankly to John Overton:

> "The powers of fortune may cause me to continue
> in a political life for one more session, but not my
> wishes. I have experienced more disquietude in a
> political life than all the advantages derived from
> it can compensate for and I assure you that my
> political life will be a short one."

That his "disquietude" was caused primarily by the subtle
thrusts at the Robards affair from which he, and through him
Rachel, never would escape, John Overton did not doubt.

However, no sooner had he resigned from the Senate that
he was elected to the State Supreme Court. Rachel was delighted. The trips to Knoxville were nothing compared to
the long absences in Philadelphia, the nation's capital. Besides, the new office gave Judge Jackson ample time for
much he must accomplish if he were to have peace of mind.
The last of the old indebtedness caused by the Allison failure
must be cleaned up; the stock in his stables must be im-
proved; he and Rachel must have more time together. They
were thirty-one now, in the early afternoon of their lives,
and that part of Andrew's complex nature that loved quiet

country living as much as Rachel did, bade him to take time now to enjoy it. A political career could follow . . . there was time enough.

Rachel was as lithe and slender as she had been ten years earlier and Andrew often watched her as she sat at Jane Hays's little shining harpsichord, a rapt expression on her face, swaying to the sunny tunes she played. Sometimes Jane played and Rachel, Andrew, and any other young neighbors who happened to be there, danced the gay schottisches and waltzes.

One day he came into the room where she sat sewing the great length of black material for his judge's robes and took the work out of her hands.

"Come and see something I think my wife will like," he invited, grinning like a suddenly shy small boy.

Rachel laughed happily up at him — she had not felt in such good spirits in years.

"Having kept your wife from the front of the house all morning," she mocked, "and having permitted such clattering and banging as I've never heard, I'll be delighted to be a witness, Your Honor."

He bent to kiss the tip of her pretty nose, took her hand and led her to the closed door of the parlour. Then with a characteristic toss of his head, he opened the door and stood aside, bowing her in with a flourish.

Rachel stepped past him into the room and gasped. Facing her across the far corner stood a beautiful pianoforte of polished rosewood. On it, invitingly open, lay Andrew's flute case and the music rack held his small book of flute music.

"Andrew! Oh, *how* beautiful! You dear extravagant darling!" Her arms went around his neck, her kisses were warm on his lips and cheeks. "Thank you . . . thank you! Now we can play 'The Campbells are coming' and 'Within a Mile' and the rest. Let's try one now — I can't wait!"

She slid on to the tufted stool, running her fingers delightedly over the keys, and Andrew took up his flute. (They could not know that more than a hundred years later another great American, Franklin Delano Roosevelt, would visit their home and hear music taken from that very book.)

The evenings were gayer now. Also, Andrew had time to devote to studying military science, a subject which was interesting him increasingly. Rachel loved to play her pianoforte softly while he read, or again to sit sewing so close beside him that they could use the same lamp.

Content though she was, she knew that complete happiness probably would always elude her and the man she loved. Though Jane's little daughter, Rachel Hays, was often at *Hunter's Hill* for days at a time, no children of their own came to fill the room Rachel always thought of as the nursery. Again, the slander against Rachel would subside like a camp fire quenched by rain, only to burst into crackling flame again when they felt it must be permanently extinguished.

Tennessee had grown from a settlement of two hundred people to a thriving state with a population of more than one hundred thousand souls. The wilderness was cleared and prosperous farms and settlements replaced the trackless forests. Both Rachel and Andrew knew that the majority of the people were their friends — there was even a Jackson County now — but here and there a political enemy of Andrew's would head a whispering campaign. When occasionally she drove with her husband on his circuit, Rachel could not force herself to enter a crowded room filled with strangers without instinctively shrinking. Were these friends? Or was there an enemy here who had heard the twelve-year-old story and would use it against them? Would they ever be free?

Chapter 9

THE HERMITAGE

WITH the passing of the years Rachel often marveled at her husband's vast fund of nervous energy — marveled and sometimes worried. Considerate and courteous always, Jackson nevertheless permitted his temper more and more to get the better of him and his political enemies were quick to make capital of his failing. If only, Rachel thought, watching him bruising himself against the barbs of his ambition and patriotic zeal, if only he could be satisfied with the rich abundance he already had! His salary as Judge of the State Supreme Court was good; his stores were doing well; the farm was flourishing; the colts in his stables were made of

133

the stuff from which great racers spring. But this was not
enough.

Andrew loved military science and had collected a fine
library on the subject. His name again had been put up for
Congress but he refused to run. He was enjoying the bench
but more than that, he was watching the position of com-
manding officer of the State Militia. The present commander,
Major General Conway, was very ill. When he died former
Governor John Sevier had his name entered as a candidate.
So did Andrew Jackson.

Jackson's election as Major General in command of the
Army of Tennessee incurred for him the bitter enmity of
the defeated Sevier. Before Rachel he treated it lightly but
there came a day when, inevitably, in a fit of anger, Sevier
spoke slightingly of the Jacksons' marriage.

Andrew challenged him to a duel, but friends persuaded
him to drop the matter as Sevier, beside being an old friend
of both the Jackson and Donelson families, was no longer a
young man. Should he be wounded — or killed — in the duel,
they pointed out, the public reaction would be fatal to Jackson's career. Rachel could not help hearing of it and the
knowledge of the whole wretched affair turned her heart-
sick. She knew now that her marriage to him was to be used
as a weapon against her husband.

His career was receiving its first sharp check, and through
John Sevier who had been elected Governor. So, Sevier
chuckled to himself, this young hothead thought he could
win command of the State Militia and flaunt his victory in

the face of the older, wiser men, did he? Well, well. . . .

Probably no man in American military history regardless of rank, took greater pride in his work than did Andrew Jackson when he began the training of his men. Rachel watched him with the tender, almost rueful expression of a mother watching a child proudly laboring over a difficult play project. Perfection was his goal and to that end he gave of his time, of himself. The Army of Tennessee — she loved hearing him say it, tossing his head a bit because he was so moved himself whenever he thought of it — the Army of Tennesse would be the best trained, the best equipped in the United States. Let no man doubt it.

There were two divisions, the eastern and the western, and their joint commander visualized them as a single mighty unit that could give a magnificent account of itself anywhere, under any circumstances.

The Louisiana Purchase was rousing both the Spanish and the Americans in the district, and the Federal Government decided it wise to send a small complement of soldiers down to maintain order. Among the states called upon for military service was Tennessee.

Andrew Jackson waited for his orders and meanwhile put his desk in order. The court docket was full but this could be handled; the orderly movement of the Army of Tennessee must come first. For this he had striven and at last the moment he had dreamed of so often was here. Time ticked on. Rachel tried to hide her nervousness, and then one afternoon she saw him coming up the drive. His body was strangely slumped in the saddle, his hands not on the reins but lying along his horse's neck. He slid to the ground and came slowly up the steps. She ran to meet him.

"Darling, what is it? What is wrong?"

He shook his head and walked into the house and dropped into his armchair, his whole body slack, eyes staring before him.

Again Rachel tried. On her knees beside his chair, she took his hand in both hers, laid her cheek against it. "Tell me, dear."

Andrew cleared his throat, tried, shook his head, and finally brought out, "I . . . Sevier . . . my command. . . ."

"Yes, go on." Rachel's heart pounded, her temples seemed about to burst, her whole body pulsated with the premonition that swept her like an icy wind. "What happened, Andrew?"

He raised his head and she could have cried for the black despair in his eyes. "John Sevier has put William Cocke — he used to be Senator — in charge of my eastern division and is sending him to Louisiana. No need, he says, for me to go. My western division stays here and twiddles its thumbs; I along with them. Sevier can't forgive me for getting the command; the duel's being canceled humiliated him; now, as Governor, he's getting even."

"But surely John Sevier's too big a man to carry a grudge to such lengths, dear. . . ."

Andrew smiled bitterly. "We're enemies," he said tonelessly, "and all's fair. . . ."

Rachel caught her breath. They were enemies . . . there was to have been a duel which was canceled and so a man was humiliated . . . and she had been the cause of the canceled duel. Truly, the thread of Lewis Robards's vengeance was very long and interwoven with every facet of her life and Andrew's. For the first time in all their years together she could not, try as she would, find words to comfort her husband. Her own heart was too heavy. It would have been heavier still if she had known how often the just and wise decisions of Judge Jackson were being openly criticized by the Governor. Thus, while his pride was being hurt, his self confidence was being undermined as well. She could only stand by, trying by her love and faith to restore his own faith in himself and in his fellow men.

Those were strange years for both Rachel and Andrew Jackson. The years 1803 and 1804 brought changes which neither could have foreseen. A governor was to be appointed to the new American territory of Orleans, that part of the Purchase lying south of Mississippi Territory and the thirty-third parallel. Thomas Jefferson was President. Andrew Jackson was weary of the Cumberland with its continuous slurs at the wife he adored. He had loved the Cumberland, but now, he told himself, he hated it and the crudities for which it stood. He would send or take his credentials to the President with whom he was on the best of terms, then — for he was sure of the appointment — he and Rachel would make a new home in more gracious suroundings. She would be the First Lady of New Orleans, beyond the touch of slander and hurt. His financial problems, too, would be solved.

The whole nation was in the throes of a great land speculation spree, Andrew Jackson like many another man of his day, was rich in land and in the possessions which a promissory note might obtain. Honorable always, he paid his debts to the best of his ability, with every expectancy of clearing them all eventually. This was the generally accepted method of doing business on the frontiers. Generosity was often a stumbling block to Andrew for his warm, impulsive nature would not permit him to refuse help in any quarter where he might find the need. But now, with a chance presented to him to buy a parcel of land "in the Ellenoise" cheaply, he sent his friend John Coffee, to offer as much as $35,000 for the tract — all on his personal note. Meanwhile he would go to Washington, the new seat of the Government, to present his credentials. From Washington he would go to Philadelphia to buy wares for his stores and several delicate pieces of furniture he thought Rachel would like for *Hunter's Hill* — or for the executive mansion of the new Governor of New Orleans.

However, when he reached the new capital on the Potomac, he learned that the President had just received word of the death of his younger daughter, Polly, Mrs. Eppes, and was preparing to leave for Virginia. Jackson had counted so on seeing Jefferson, discussing the New Orleans matter with him, but he could not bring himself to intrude upon the great man at such a time, even to offer sympathy, lest his motives be misunderstood. As he wrote John Coffee:

> "Under present circumstances my feeling would not consent to pay my respects to him lest it might be construed into the conduct of a courtier and my visit might have created such sensations in his mind. I therefore passed on without calling. Of all ideas to me it is the most humiliating to be thought to cringe to power to obtain a favor or an appointment."

A few days later he was to learn that William Charles Cole Claiborne had been appointed Governor General of the Territory of Orleans. Jackson returned to *Hunter's Hill* in a desperate state of mind. Suddenly everything, *everything* seemed to be slipping out of his grasp. By the time he had paid the freight charges on his merchandise which arrived by flatboat shortly after he did, Andrew Jackson's pockets were empty though his strongbox still bulged with notes he was unable to collect.

What this fiery, frustrated man would have done with a less understanding wife it is hard to say. Had he been less proud, less the idealist, he might with complete diplomacy have called upon the President, offered condolences, and at least have brought himself even momentarily to the attention of the Chief Executive. He and Rachel might even then have been on their way to prosperity and comparative peace of mind in the Deep South.

But there were no words of condemnation from the gentle, dark-eyed woman waiting for him at *Hunter's Hill*. They talked far into the night. *Hunter's Hill* must go if debts were to be honorably discharged, and with it must go certain cherished possessions and some fine livestock. The gray face of the dawn was looking in at the windows, mocking the lamplight when Andrew finally got to his feet, knocked the ashes from his pipe, and came around the table to Rachel's side. He put his finger under her chin and tilted her face up.

"I've tried so hard, darling, but I've got us in an awful mess," he said hoarsely.

She met his eyes smilingly, willing her own not to blur with tears. "You tried and you've won in doing what seemed right at the time, dear," she said. "We're not too old to start over again. Any place on earth, so long as you are there, will be a perfect home for me."

And then, in spite of her efforts, the tears came, tears of grief for the husband she loved so, the man who so often defeated his own high purpose. She clung to him, crying her heart out. Finally he blew out the lamp, and hand in hand, the two tired people walked through the first pink glow of morning and climbed the stairs to bed.

The beloved pianoforte, the mahogany chest, the grand-father's clock, and several other pieces of furniture were loaded on the wagon that would take them to their new home. Andrew rode with the furniture. Rachel followed with the two house servants in the coach, and bringing up the rear the field hands with the kitchenware, the supplies and the livestock that remained.

They were going to *The Hermitage*, an acreage about a mile distant, which Andrew had bought some years earlier.

The land was rolling and fertile, but the dwelling itself would have discouraged a less optimistic woman than Rachel. It had been a trading post, a blockhouse, its logs well matched, its squat chimney attesting the huge fireplace inside. There was one enormous room on the first floor and there were two on the second, reached by a steep flight of narrow stairs.

Rachel looked about, glimpsing the smoked overhead beams, the porthole windows which must be enlarged to let in more sunlight, the broad expanse of clay-chinked wall where book shelves would be built to hold the library Andrew had been collecting. At present the place was gray with the dust of years and fuzzy with cobwebs, but Rachel turned to Andrew with clasped hands, her eyes shining.

"I declare, it's lovely, lovely! Just wait until Trudie and Tom have scrubbed it and we have a fire on the hearth! Andrew, this is the dearest home of all!"

"It's only a store, built during the worst of the Indian raids," he answered. "It's sturdy, but not beautiful, my wife, not beautiful."

But Rachel persisted. "Wait and see," she laughed and hurried to the door to check on what progress was being made with the unloading. Once more there was a song in her heart. *Hunter's Hill* had been impressive but it had brought her little real happiness. As for Andrew, he had been there so seldom as to seem more a guest than the host when they entertained their friends. Now they were really at home again, together, surrounded by the things they loved best.

Fortunately for them, John Coffee had been unable to buy

the land in "the Ellenoise" and Rachel sighed with relief when she heard it. Perhaps now life would run smoothly for a while at least. Yet scarcely were they settled when Samuel, the best loved brother, was ambushed and killed much as his father had been, either by Indians or highwaymen, while hunting in an unfamiliar region.

Recovering from the first numbing shock, Rachel wondered dimly at the stabbing pain in her heart. Not since a day years earlier had she known that particular suffocating agony. It passed, however, and she set about helping Polly, Samuel's wife, with her three little boys.

Young Andy was just four. After the funeral, as the Jacksons were taking their leave, Andy refused to release Rachel's hand. "Let me go with you, Aunt Rachel," he coaxed. "Please let me!"

She looked down into the brown eyes so like Samuel's and then at Polly. Polly nodded, wadding her handkerchief over tear-swollen eyes. "My hands are going to be mighty full with the other two," she said brokenly. "Andy's a good child — he'll not make you much trouble. Take him if you want him."

Andrew sat down on his heels and drew the little boy to him. "Sure you want to come and help me make a fine farm over at *The Hermitage,* son?" he asked seriously, noting the child's steady gaze, the proud lift of his head.

Andy took a deep breath. "Yes, sir. Certain sure. I'll fetch me my coon cap."

Andrew stifled a smile and patted the sturdy little shoul-

der. "That's the boy! A coon cap's a mighty fine thing to own. Get it and then you and I'll take Aunt Rachel home."

So through the frosty autumn twilight Andrew and Rachel walked homeward with a little boy's hands clasped in theirs. Over his head they smiled at each other in perfect understanding. A child had come to them. *The Hermitage* would never be without the sound of pounding young feet or a child's laughter.

That night as she tucked Andy into bed, with his beloved coon cap on the pillow beside him, Rachel thought how full of unexpected events the years 1803 and 1804 had been. Some had been grave, some very good, and all she was certain as she tiptoed out of the room, all were indispensable parts of the pattern that was shaping her life and Andrew's.

"God give me grace — God give me faith to see Thy hand in all things," she whispered, and went down to join her husband before the fire.

Chapter 10

THE PASSING YEARS

OFTEN during the twenty years that followed Rachel looked
back upon what had gone before and thought what a prelude
it had been to the drama which now took over her hus-
band's life and her own. The months aboard the *Adventure;*
her girlhood in Kentucky; the black years as the wife of
Lewis Robards; the sunny, busy years so filled with pride as
Andrew became Attorney General at twenty-one, United
States Senator at thirty-one, then Judge of the State Supreme
Court, and General in command of the State Militia; *Poplar
Grove; Hunter's Hill;* and now *The Hermitage.* These would
have filled an average lifetime. In the crowded lives of
Rachel and Andrew Jackson, however, they formed only the
foundation upon which the main structure of their days was
built.

Andrew now laid out his race course with John Coffee for a partner, and soon he was prosperous once more. But out of the race track came a new difficulty, rather a variation of an old one. At one of the major races of the season Andrew and a young man named Charles Dickinson had a dispute over the forfeiture of a race. Andrew left the track but learned almost at once that Dickinson who had been drinking, had spoken of Rachel and of their marriage in coarse terms. It was the unforgivable sin. He challenged Dickinson to a duel.

It was spring — 1806 — and on a certain morning in May the air about *The Hermitage* was heavy with the scent of wild lilac and sweet with the songs of waking birds. The sun had not yet risen when Rachel walked with Andrew to the hitching post where his horse stood waiting. He would meet General Tom Overton, John Overton's brother, who was acting as his second, in Nashville. Since Tennessee frowned on dueling, they would ride across the border into Kentucky. At a chosen spot on the Red River they would meet Dickinson and his second.

Andrew gathered up the reins, turned and scooped Rachel into his arms. "Good-by, sweetheart," he whispered against her hair. "Don't worry. Dickinson's a good shot but so am I. I'll be home for supper the day after tomorrow, so put on one of your prettiest dresses and be waiting here for me. Now good-by. . . ." He kissed her and swung himself into the saddle.

"Good-by . . . good-by, my darling. . . ."

She watched him go, longing to run after him, to tell him how much she loved him, how indelibly etched upon her heart was the memory of every moment they had shared. Why, *why*, she wondered, walking back at last across the dew-soaked grass, why must the cruel, senseless lashing out at her for something of which she was wholly innocent, go on? How many years had it been — fifteen? — since she and Andrew had been married and had gone to Bayou Pierre on their honeymoon. They had been so happy, so humble in their gratitude for the happiness vouchsafed them. Yet scarcely a full year had passed since then without its shameful vilifying from one quarter or another. And now Andrew. . . . She shuddered away from the fear that touched her, ashamed of her own morbidness.

As she approached the house, in spite of herself she broke into soft chuckles of amusement. Framed in the open doorway stood Andy. Draped casually over his nightshirt and trailing behind him, was the patchwork quilt from his bed, and on his head at a rakish angle, sat the coon cap. He might, Rachel thought as she hurried to him, have been a picture whose artist had called his finished work *The New Century Steps Forth*.

"Andy, go back to bed, dear," she counseled. "It's still much too early to get up. You'll take cold." She sought to turn him about, take him indoors.

But small Andy looked up at his aunt with a faintly defiant expression, his feet firmly planted. "Where did my Uncle Andrew go?" he queried anxiously.

"He went to Kentucky. Come — inside, son." She picked up his trailing quilt and pushed him gently before her, and perforce Andy obeyed.

But he was not satisfied. "I was fixin' to go with him," he said, "only I couldn't get down in time. My cap got lost. . . . He'll be lonely 'thout me," he added so soberly that for a moment Rachel thought he was going to cry. She sat down and gathered him, cap, quilt, and all, onto her lap and held him close in the early morning chill.

"Uncle Andrew's meeting another gentleman in Nashville, dear," she comforted. "He won't be lonely, really he won't."

"Sure 'nough?"

"Sure 'nough," she promised. She felt the little body relax against her; the coon cap sagged tipsily, the intrepid scout and self-appointed guardian of uncles was asleep.

All through that day and the next she waited and prayed. And in Kentucky a duel was fought, destined to be linked with the name of Andrew Jackson forever thereafter.

The opponents stood at twenty-four paces. At the word "Fire!" each man raised his pistol, aimed and fired. Dickinson, well known for his spectacular marksmanship, fired quickly, virtually as the command was given. Jackson, more deliberate, and conscious that he had been struck in the shoulder, aimed and pulled the trigger. It stopped at half-cock. He pulled it again, the shot rang out and Dickinson fell, mortally wounded. Only then did Tom Overton realize that Jackson was swaying on his feet in a pool of blood, and insisted that the physician present examine him.

"It's nothing, Jackson declared, "nothing but a scratch. Let's start for home, Tom."

So reluctantly Overton lifted the wounded man into the saddle and the long ride back to *The Hermitage* began. Dickinson lingered through the day but died before midnight.

Rachel, in the pink organdie frock she knew Andrew loved, stood at the mounting block which commanded a view of the road. And at last she saw the little cavalcade approaching, Andrew, his arm in a sling, riding between Tom Overton and the doctor. She ran to him but Overton waved her back and together the two men helped Andrew into the house and to bed. There, while the wound was being redressed, they took turns telling her about the strange duel.

"You see, Ma'am," Overton explained, "General Jackson and Mr. Dickinson stood sidewise to each other. The General's coat is loose, you know, and it billowed out a little right on a line with his heart — where Dickinson was aiming. Well, Ma'am, Dickinson's aim was perfect but he shot at a *bulge of cloth*, and by the time he'd collected himself the General's second pull on the trigger had put a bullet in his stomach. That's how simple it was. When we passed through Nashville on the way home, word had come in that Dickinson was sinking."

Rachel felt suddenly sick. A man was dying — dying by her husband's bullet, and because of her. "God pity his poor young wife and the new baby," she whispered, and in her heart an echo sounded: "And pity us, too."

Rachel had much to trouble her that summer. Andrew's shoulder was slow in healing; he refused to let it be known how seriously wounded he actually had been, with the result that he was looked upon by many people as a bully who had taken advantage of a younger man's inexperience. It was harvest time and while Andrew lay helpless and frustrated on his bed, she alone was responsible for the amount of work the field hands accomplished.

Often, walking or riding across the fields, hat tipped low against the blinding heat, she was conscious of an undercurrent of unease in all her thinking, and a name persistently intruded itself upon even her busiest moments. That name was Aaron Burr.

How clearly she remembered Andrew's enthusiastic description of the man when they both had been members of the Senate back in 1797. Senator Burr had given a dinner which Andrew loved to describe as the most lavish he ever had attended and his host as the most brilliant conversationalist he ever had listened to. Rachel recalled how at the time it had occured to her that the man sounded unduly opinionated but she refrained from saying so to Andrew.

In 1800 Burr became Vice President when both he and Thomas Jefferson had run for the Presidency and Jefferson had won after the election had been thrown into the House of Representatives. Embittered, Burr ran for the Governorship of New York following his term as Vice President. But here again he was defeated and in his revolt against failure, he accused Alexander Hamilton, the eminent statesman, of having plotted his political downfall. He killed Hamilton in a duel in the summer of 1804. Hamilton, who shot in the air, became something of a popular martyr.

Walking between rows of cotton pickers, Rachel remembered the peculiar combination of pleasure and dread she felt when, just a year ago, Andrew had suggested they entertain Aaron Burr at dinner, invite a dozen or more of the most socially prominent people of Nashville to meet him. His term as Vice President was ended, the Governorship had not materialized. Just what, she asked, was Colonel Burr doing in Tennessee? He seemed to tell so many extremely interesting stories about his plans, but exactly *what were they*?

The dinner party had been a great success. Rachel herself had enjoyed it, looking her prettiest, returning quip for quip as her guest of honor charmed everyone and showed her his most flattering attention. Still, there had been something — what was it? — a barrier of some sort, a distinct feeling of distaste that swept over her whenever she met his bantering smile. Was it the knowledge that here at her table sat a man who had killed a fellow being? Duels were not unusual; then what was it? Among Dickinson's friends feeling was running high. Was it possible they felt about Andrew as she had about Aaron Burr?

Thus the hot summer dragged its dusty skirts through field and orchard and vanished one day in late September when torrential rain swept across the Cumberland. Rumors were afoot that Aaron Burr was plotting to raise a fleet, sail south and conquer Mexico, making himself its ruler.

Whether or not his intentions were treasonable never has been established, but the Jacksons were both angry and worried. Earlier Burr had ordered flatboats from Andrew who had had them built and equipped, believing them to be for the United States Government. Burr was arrested on suspicion of treason. However, the charges were dismissed and one day he presented himself at *The Hermitage*. Andrew was absent from home but Rachel met the Colonel without embarrassment. She stood firmly in the doorway.

"My husband is not here at the moment, Colonel Burr," she told him unsmilingly, and added that she trusted and believed the nearby tavern would make him comfortable. Much as she disliked hurting any living being, Rachel Jackson was equally determined that no man who, either by intent or through stupidity, had ensnared her husband in a questionable scheme should be a guest in their home.

The Jacksons were never to know whether or not Aaron Burr was an arch plotter. Andrew's more impressionable nature refused to be entirely convinced that so eloquent a patriotic speaker could be guilty of double dealing. Rachel, more realistic, never got over her first instinctive distrust of the man. But when later Colonel Burr was re-indicted, for high misdemeanor this time, she held her counsel. However, she knew that Andrew's continued championship of Burr would be used against him should he decide to re-enter politics. It was.

It was on a bitter day in January — 1810 — that Severn

Donelson who had settled on a tract not far from *The Hermitage,* pushed open the door of the big living room and, trailing a path of snowy footsteps, tramped across the room to where Rachel sat reading to Andy. His habitually sallow face was drawn, his eyes dark caverns of misery.

"Rachel, could you come?" he burst out without preliminaries. "Lizabeth is terribly sick. Viney's caring for her but things aren't going well . . . ."

Rachel closed her book. "Run along to Trudie like a good boy, Andy," she said, "and when Uncle Andrew comes tell him I've gone to Uncle Severn's — that Aunt Lizabeth is sick." She reached for her bonnet and heavy winter shawl, pulled on her boots, and in less than ten minutes was crunching along over the hard snow beside her brother.

"We have a little boy, Rachel," Severn said in a matter-of-fact tone as they hurried along. "He was born an hour ago, but something's wrong — Lizabeth's had five children, but this — well, maybe you'll know what to do. You always do," he ended on a helpless, hopeful note.

Rachel patted his arm. "Lizabeth 'll be all right, Sev. Try not to worry," she re-assured him.

As they opened the door they heard Viney's jubilant shout: "Bless de Lawd, Miss Lizabeth! We got *another* li'l boy!"

Rachel tossed her bonnet and shawl at Severn, blew on her cold hands, and ran into the bedroom. "Lizabeth, darling," laughter bubbled in her voice as she looked from the bed to the low chair beside the fire where fat Viney sat bathing something that made mewing sounds like a kitten. In a blanket-filled basket beside her another mewing voice joined in . . . "Lizabeth, honey," she looked at the young-old face on the pillow and smoothed back the straggling hair, "you have little twin boys! Isn't that wonderful?"

For an instant she closed her own eyes before her sister-in-law's brave effort to smile. Then tears filled the young mother's eyes and poured down her thin cheeks as she clung to Rachel's hand. "What *am* I to do with two new babies when I've not the strength to care rightly for one?" she sobbed. "And there are five others besides, you know. Rachel, sister, you've wanted children so. . . . *Could* you take this last little boy for your own?"

There was silence in the room broken only by the minute snuffling sounds from the babies. Severn, standing on the other side of the bed, looked from his sister to his wife and back again. "If you would, Rachel, and if Andrew was of a like mind and would adopt the little fellow, give him th' Jackson name, I'd feel it was a blessing from th' Almighty."

Rachel's mind was in a tumult, her thoughts trying to adjust circumstance to fact. She had longed so for a child of her own across the years. Andy was a nephew who at any time might return to his mother, dearly though they loved him. At forty-one she was being presented with a son to call her own, a child with Donelson blood in its veins. What would Andrew say? But she knew. He loved children so; he, too, would welcome a son. She smiled from Severn to Lizabeth, her cheeks flushed, her eyes dark and shining with a new joy.

"I'll take him," she said. "My Becky has a new baby; she'll nurse him."

So it came about that the tiny boy was duly adopted and baptized and given the name Andrew Jackson, Jr. Jackson fairly worshipped the child, and young Andy, eight now, far from feeling any jealousy, took a proprietary interest in his little cousin.

"He's a captain, sure 'nough," he told John Overton, "a real captain."

Chapter 11

TOGETHER

ON JUNE 21, 1812, when little Andrew Jackson Jr. was a two-and-a-half year old toddler, the United States declared war on Great Britain.

Andrew Jackson spent his own money on the best rifles, the finest equipment obtainable. His troops, twenty-five hundred strong, were well trained and waiting for orders either from Washington or from the Governor at Knoxville. Still, just as he had waited years earlier to be sent to Mississippi, so now he marked off the days while Detroit fell to the British and still no word came.

When he offered to march a thousand men to re-take Detroit, his offer was ignored. Desperate, he watched while the ranks of the enemy were swelled by thousands of Creek Indians, thus bringing back all the horrors of Indian warfare. Sick at heart, he saw the first fine enthusiasm of his own troops waver as the stalemate continued into the autumn.

In New York Aaron Burr told his young friend, Martin Van Buren, "I'll tell you why they don't employ Jackson. It's because he's a friend of mine."

This was four years after Burr's sensational acquittal. He had just returned from Europe, a tired, disillusioned man in threadbare, immaculate clothes. Whatever his intentions years earlier treasonable or not, he was always to remember Andrew Jackson's friendliness. Jackson had believed in him — had believed him to be a sincere patriot.

The effect upon General Jackson of the snubs dealt him by the Federal Government was devastating. Rachel was beside herself with worry as she watched him grow thinner, more taciturn with the passing days while the British he hated so penetrated deeper into his country. Governor Willie Blount was Jackson's friend and he, too, was torn yet helpless in the face of the Administration's continued unwillingness to accept his services.

At last, with courage that must have startled his staff, the Governor took matters into his own hands and commissioned him Major General of Volunteers and ordered him to move his troops with all possible speed to New Orleans to reinforce Brigadier General James Wilkinson, a man whom Jackson always had distrusted.

Nevertheless, Andrew Jackson was a soldier who obeyed orders, and immediately he set about mustering his men. They were encamped first in Nashville. Then, early in January Rachel watched first Colonel John Coffee ride toward Natchez at the head of his contingent, then Andrew and his infantrymen go aboard the flatboats that would carry them down the Cumberland in the same direction.

There was something comforting in knowing that these two friends were starting off simultaneously, if not together, on a common mission for their country. John Coffee who was thirty-seven and, as everyone supposed, a confirmed bachelor, had married sixteen-year-old Mary Donelson, Rachel's brother John's daughter, and the bond between the two families was very close.

Back at *The Hermitage,* Rachel was soon to learn how badly the war was going in the North — or the East as they called it then; Tennessee constantly was referred to as the West. Two regiments of Kentucky boys had been massacred by Indians; two Generals captured. It could not have happened, she told herself, if Andrew had been sent East as he had begged to be.

Then almost before he was gone — six weeks — word came that he was returning! Rachel could not believe the news when she heard it. Andrew's services had not been wanted in the first place, yet he had equipped his men and marched them over five hundred miles. Now he was being sent home, he and these same men. Rachel read the copy of the dispatch again:

War Department, Feb. 5, 1813

Sir:

The Causes for embodying . . . the Corps under your command having ceased to exist, you will on receipt of this letter consider it dismissed from public service and deliver over to Major General Wilkinson all articles of public property. . . ." Accept for yourself and the Corps the thanks of the President of the United States. I have the honor to be

Your obedient servant —

It was signed by the new Secretary of War, John Armstrong.

What did it mean? Why? Why? Why? The dismissal came as an answer to Andrew's urgent plea to be sent to the northern front where in Canada defeat was piling up on defeat, while in the Deep South where he was encamped, there was comparative quiet. Literally he was being booted out!

But again Andrew Jackson's loftiness of spirit shone forth. He had a gruelling march ahead of him with his men, some of them wounded, many sick, and General Wilkinson allowing rations for only a fortnight. Jackson signed notes for wagons, horses, rations. All told he spent more than a thousand dollars of his own money for the sick. *Somehow,* by *some* means, he was determined to get his "boys" home. And this he did, walking most of the way himself and earning the affectionate nickname "Old Hickory."

"He's tough, tough as hickory," one wounded soldier told another, watching from the comparative warmth of their wagon as the General slogged along on foot in the bitter wind. So "Hickory" he became, but long before Nashville was reached the soubriquet had been changed affectionately to "Old Hickory" and it was as "Old Hickory" that General Jackson received the acclaim of Tennessee.

Meanwhile, in Mississippi Territory, four hundred persons had been massacred by Creeks in the employ of the British. Governor Blount must have been embarrassed, indeed, when he arrived in person to beg Jackson to lead an army against them.

Again Old Hickory marshaled his troops and this time, with provisions from *The Hermitage* supplementing regulation army rations, he set forth, retracing his steps over the long trail south. Hunger and mutiny stalked beside him; illness weakened him so that at times he could not leave his cot. Nevertheless, by careful strategy he surprised the Indians, routing them, killing more than three hundred.

At home Rachel struggled with the plantation and with a severe attack of grippe. But word of the General's smashing victories in Emuckfaw and Enotachopco kept her smiling even when her teeth chattered with the chills that racked her. Here were victories, not retreats! Here was a General, not a captive of the enemy but a leader who stormed up and down his embattled lines, encouraging, inspiring his men, winning battles in the face of every known form of Indian cunning. And as word of his victories spread, new volunteers came streaming into battle until there came the final engagement at historic Horseshoe Bend where the Creek nation was vanquished and the British guns silenced.

In the midst of the Indian retreat Jackson's heart was touched by the sight of an Indian child in distress. Inevitably as Creek encampments were destroyed, women and children, too, suffered and occasionally were killed. The General, walk-

ing back to his quarters after the battle of Horseshoe Bend,
saw a little boy of about three standing alone, bewildered,
just beyond the line of the fleeing Creeks. Jackson spoke to
him but received only a stoic, round-eyed stare. The Indian
women refused to take him, for, said they, his parents both
had been killed so why not kill him, too, since a child alone
was a burden?

General Jackson had been wounded in one arm. With his
good hand he took from his pocket some brown sugar,
melted it in a cup of water from his canteen, and gave it to
the boy. Light came into the black eyes, lips smacked in
appreciation over the sweet goodness in the cup, and the
faintest shadow of a smile slid for just an instant over the
round little face, then disappeared again.

Through Quals, his Indian interpreter, Jackson learned the
child's name was Lincoyer; and Rachel must have smiled a
little uncertainly over the closing paragraph of a letter she
received toward the end of December, 1813:

> "I have directed Major White to carry to you the
> little Lincoyer. . . . Charity and Christianity says
> he ought to be taken care of and I send him to my
> little Andrew and I hope you will adopt him as one
> of our family."

I've wanted children, she thought, folding the letter, and
now I shall have three: Samuel's Andy, Severn's Andrew Jr.,
and now a poor Creek mother's little Lincoyer. God bless
them all.

Jackson's peace terms with the Creeks have been called unnecessarily harsh; the surrender of twenty-three million acres of Creek land. Harsh it may have been, but it was a clean cut, not a slow treacherous withdrawal. Thirty-six chiefs signed the treaty. Truly he merited the name they gave him: Sharp Knife. Added to Old Hickory it was a significant description of the man whose deeply tender nature so few understood.

General Jackson, since success begets success, was the man of the hour. There was talk of making him Governor of Tennessee, but the following May — 1814 — there came an offer much more attractive to the master of *The Hermitage*. A letter from the Secretary of War announced the resignation of Major General Harrison and the placing of Jackson's name in the vacancy thus created. At last, after so many disappointments, so many heartbreaking waits in the past, here was the one prize above all others which he would have sought eagerly, coming to him without his having had the slightest suspicion that it was being considered.

His appointment could not have come at a more significant time. The Creek war under British dictate was over, true, but from elsewhere in the country the news was not good. The Capital in Washington had been burned; the President's house, the Treasury and Department of State buildings were in ashes; the city was in British hands. Now British ships were anchored off the Florida coast.

History tells how General Jackson's troops routed the

British fleet, then marched on to Pensacola — again on rations he provided largely with his own money. Pensacola was captured and the enemy driven into the sea — and this by the American patriot whose services the War Department had repeatedly refused.

Then on to New Orleans. The brilliance of Jackson's strategy there and the steady, relentless marksmanship of his frontier fighters, ended in the complete collapse of the enemy forces. The battle of New Orleans was won; the British thoroughly beaten, got back to their distant ships as best they could, and Andrew Jackson was the nation's idol.

Rachel's hands lay idle in her lap as she sat at the open window looking out over the rolling acres of *The Hermitage*. So much had happened since Andrew's great victory in New Orleans. She had been at his side to receive the plaudits of the people who came from every part of Louisiana to show their appreciation. With grace she had worn the costly gowns made for the round of entertainments in their honor and more than once had caught her husband's look of pride. The whole New Orleans experience had been thrilling, warmly satisfying, but home, the blessed peace and seclusion of home — these were sweeter still. And as she sat looking out into the cool May sunshine she found herself wondering about something she had heard a gentleman say at one of the gayest of the New Orleans dinners.

"You know, Mrs. Jackson," he had exclaimed under cover of the chatter buzzing around them, "they say there's a straight road running from New Orleans to Washington."

For a moment she did not understand and when she did and made a laughing rejoinder, her heart seemed to have turned to lead. Washington — Andrew President! Oh, no, please not that!

But Andrew must never know how she felt. With every means at her command, if the Presidency was really what he wanted, she must help him attain it. Home was what she wanted though, home with Andrew and the boys and all the fair green world of the Cumberland to call their sanctum. How little time across all the years she and Andrew actually had been together! They were forty-eight now. Rachel had grown plump. She often wished the miniature she had had painted for Andrew just before New Orleans had been done fifteen years sooner. Then looking at her husband's straight, gaunt figure, his face deeply lined, his shock of redish hair streaked with gray, she knew the miniature was right. To the end of his life Andrew Jackson wore it on a silver chain around his neck. His Rachel, forever the most beautiful, forever the greatly beloved.

In the autumn they went together to Washington where Andrew transacted post war business and Rachel met Thomas Jefferson, had tea with beautiful, haughty Mrs. James Monroe, and thought she never had seen an uglier spot than the nation's barren mud-clogged capital city.

Back at home again, Andrew began making plans for a larger house. Little progress had been made on the actual building, though, when he was ordered into the Indian

country again and Rachel was left with the supervision of
the work. She smiled a little to herself thinking how often
throughout the years she had taken over the lighting and
tending of the home fires.

The years crowded in. James Monroe, now President, was
their first guest in the new *Hermitage;* Robert Hays died
suddenly and Jane went to live with a married son in Texas;
Andy was a law student at Transilvania University in Kentucky; Andrew Jr. enrolled at Cumberland College in Nashville, and Lincoyer attending a school near *The Hermitage.*
Sometimes the fine new house seemed much too big. Then
little Andrew Hutchings, Rachel's sister Catherine's grand-
son, came to live at the plantation following the death of his
father. So again there was a little boy to trot muddy boots
across the polished floors, to ride his fat pony beside Rachel's
horse across the fields. There were three young Andrews
now, yet when they were all together at *The Hermitage* it
became a favorite joke among them that they could tell, by
the inflection in Rachel's voice when she called, which one
of them she meant.

In March — 1821 — Jackson was appointed Governor of
the Territory of Florida. In Pensacola on July 17th Rachel
witnessed the impressive ceremony when the Spanish Governor, Jose Callava, formally presented the Spanish province
of Florida to her husband who accepted it for the United
States. Slowly the Spanish flag was lowered as the American
Stars and Stripes just as slowly rose to snap 'n the breeze on
the giant flag pole before the Governor's mansion.

But both Andrew and Rachel were eager to leave Florida and its frankly hostile populace. Andrew had accomplished the diplomatic mission on which he had been sent, so after eight months in the exotic new Territory, Old Hickory turned homeward. But politics was in the air and scarcely were the Jacksons back at *The Hermitage* when Andrew once more was elected to the Senate.

Andy was his Aunt Rachel's greatest comfort. He was just slightly older now than his father had been when together he and Rachel had made the long journey from Harrodsburg to the Cumberland — it seemed only yesterday. Andy was building a fine law practice in Nashville while courting his Cousin Emily, John Donelson's younger daughter, and Aunt Rachel had no time to be lonesome. John Overton, Judge Overton now, lived nearby, too, married to an attractive widow with a house full of girls and boys, and the Overtons were usually among *The Hermitage* guests. Rachel welcomed them all. Her days were full and happy, with young people swarming through the house and Andrew's Washington letters the brightest spots on each week.

The step from the Senate to the candidacy for President was inevitable. Jackson's complex nature seized at the challenge while turning longingly to the serenity of the plantation. His love of country had been his ruling passion from boyhood; anything even remotely concerned with that country's welfare had precedence over every other interest. Now he was being sought for the highest office in the land. Rachel who secretly shuddered at the possibility of being First Lady with all that position entailed, nonetheless gave him every encouragement. They drove to Washington in November — 1824 — taking with them Andy and his bride on a belated honeymoon. Andy and his Emily had been married in September.

They had been in Washington only a few hours when Rachel, resting in the sitting room of their hotel suite, chanced to pick up a newspaper. Idly turning its pages, she found herself staring at an editorial which ended with the words:

> "I make a solemn appeal to the reflecting part of the community, and beg of them to ponder well before they place their tickets in the box, how they can justify it to themselves and posterity to place such a woman as Mrs. Jackson at the head of the female society of the United States!"

The paper slid to the floor and before Rachel's eyes the room spun in flying circles. Her breath came in sobs against the terrible pressure on her chest; her hands were like ice. "Such a woman as Mrs. Jackson!" The years so filled with love for her fellow beings, for every man, woman or lonely child to cross her path, had only this to say for her!

But when her husband came in later, he found her listening to Emily's animated description of a tea she and Andy had attended with some other young people from Tennessee. Rachel was pale but her laughter sounded happy and her eyes were unshadowed by the ache in her heart.

Andrew Jackson was defeated by John Quincy Adams, but

far from being discouraged, Old Hickory was more confident
of his own political strength, more certain of eventual victory than he ever had been. The year 1824 was a solid step-
ping stone to 1828. The tide was carrying him now; nothing
could hold him back. Newspapers throughout the country
were hailing him as the next President, and across the four
intervening years the army of his supporters grew.

Yet every army must face an opposing host, and as Andrew Jackson's election approached, the greatest campaign
of unprincipled scandelmongering ever known in the history
of the United States was launched at him — through his
wife. A vicious pamphlet published by a Thomas Arnold said
in part:

> "Anyone approving of Andrew Jackson must
> therefore declare in favor of the philosophy that
> any man wanting anyone else's pretty wife has
> nothing to do but take his pistol in one hand and
> a horsewhip in another and possess her."

Charles Hammond, owner of a Cincinnati newspaper, followed the article with another even more defamatory. The
marriage at the Green plantation thirty-six years earlier (he
declared) was illegal, and opposite Rachel Jackson's name
in huge type sprawled the ugly word ADULTERESS.

There it was, the final outrage, the unpardonable accusation. For once Jackson controlled his temper. He appointed
a committee of eighteen of the most highly respected men
in Tennessee, Judges, former ambassadors, members of the
United States Supreme Court. John Overton was chairman.

To this committee was assigned the task of searching out old records, speaking whenever possible with those who had known the Jacksons during the early days of their marriage and the year preceding it.

All this required time and meanwhile the campaign progressed. How often, lying in her bed in the evening while in his study downstairs Andrew and Judge Overton worked on campaign matters, Rachel, propped high on her pillows, tried to pray for those who were destroying her. Breathing was becoming increasingly difficult for her and she was seldom without pain. But this was Rachel's secret.

Partial vindication came as the committee searched through countless old records. But the Natchez marriage certificate could not be found, probably as none may have been considered necessary under the prevailing law, or, because as with so many of the Spanish records, it was destroyed before the American occupation.

Andrew Jackson was elected President of the United States on November 24, 1828, by an overwhelming majority over John Quincy Adams who had run for a second term. He had reached the top. The lonely boy weeping over the neat little parcel of his dead mother's clothes; the strippling binding up his bayonet slashed hands; this red-headed lad from the Waxhaws stood now in the highest position in the land. And his heart was heavy, for Rachel's secret was not wholly her own. The man who loved her suspected the truth: that she was a very sick woman.

Nashville went mad with joy over the election. "The Gen-

eral" had been elected! His beloved lady would be the nation's First Lady! What would be a fitting celebration for
these two greatly loved people? A banquet seemed the final
choice. It would be held on December 23rd at the *Nashville Inn* with Christmas decorations and proverbial Christmas turkey. There would be a Negro octette singing carols
and an orchestra playing during dinner. There would be
toasts by prominent men from the state and beyond. Every
possible honor would be done the two people who were so
much a part of the Cumberland. The inauguration would
follow in February, but first Tennessee must show its devotion.

Rachel looked deeply into Andrew's eyes as they sat before the fire in her sitting room one evening in early December.

"You know, don't you, my darling, how happy I am for
you?" she asked. She was seeing as though she never had
seen it before, how snowy white his hair had grown within
the past few months, how deep the lines about his eyes and
mouth.

He leaned over to lay his hand on hers. "I know, dear," he
answered, and then like a frightened boy, he caught her
fingers in his, crushing them until she winced, and added,
"If only one knew what was best! I'll need you so in the four
years just ahead. I'll need moments like this — just you and I
together, darling, to keep me on an even keel. Is the election
worth all the — the re-adjusting it is going to call for? Would
you rather — no, it's too late for that now. But help me,

help me bring something of our *Hermitage* life to the White House. . . . It's a part of our life I don't want to lose — I. . . ." His voice broke and sank to a whisper and in the firelight Rachel saw his cheeks were wet.

"I'll not let you lose it, dear — not ever," she promised and lifted his hand to her cheek.

Her nieces, her closest friends, all insisted she must have a truly regal wardrobe for her entry into Washington society and there must be a very special gown for the Christmas banquet in Nashville. So, measuring her time and strength carefully one against the other, Rachel let them drape the beautiful fabrics on her stout figure, trying to share their raptures over colors which were "Just *so* lovely with your dark eyes and gray hair," over lines which "do exactly the right thing for you, Aunt Rachel."

After the fittings she would drive back to *The Hermitage*, sip a cup of scalding coffee, and lie down. She usually kept her Bible beside her and found comfort in the passages she had marked: ". . . where the spirit of the Lord is, there is liberty." . . . "and whosoever believeth on Him shall not be ashamed. . . ." "even as Christ forgave you, so also do ye" . . . . "Fight the good fight of faith, lay hold on eternal life" . . . . "The Lord shall deliver me from every evil work . . .". So she would fall asleep.

On the afternoon of the twentieth, following an especially tiring fitting, Rachel told the seamstress to have the coachman bring the carriage to the *Inn* when he called for her; she was going there to rest before driving home. She went into the parlor reserved for ladies and sat down and closed her eyes. Ah, this was good . . . good. Her head drooped and she dozed. She was roused by the sound of women's voices talking. They were just beyond her line of vision but close enough for their words to reach her distinctly. Suddenly the word "Jackson" leapt out and was followed quickly by a sentence that burned into the sick woman's consciousness like white-hot metal.

"Having a low, loose-moraled woman like that Mrs. Jackson in the White House I think is an affront to every virtuous woman in the country," the voice declared.

There was a rejoinder which Rachel did not hear. She struggled to her feet as pain tore through her chest and down her left arm. Her breath came in shallow puffs like unsuccessful attempts to blow out a candle. Her bonnet slipped back, her shawl dragged the floor behind her. She stumbled a little as she walked to the door.

The carriage had just arrived and her boy, consternation twisting his round young face, ran to take her arm. "Is you sick, Miz Rachel?"

She shook her head. "Just take me home quickly, please, Jasper, then fetch the General. . . ."

Rachel could not be sure whether hours or days passed. Only one thing seemed important: Andrew was with her. Again and again she opened her eyes to find him leaning over her, not smiling, just looking — looking. Sometimes his lips moved but she could not hear the words. Or maybe she had dreamed it all and he had not said anything or even

been there. Terror would seize her. But no, the dear face
was there again and this time she did catch the words: "Forever and ever and ever I love you." She thought she answered something but could not be sure. And then she knew
nothing more.

To the man sitting beside her it was not true. She was not
dead. Dully he turned the hand he held over until it lay,
palm up, in his. The wedding ring, worn quite thin, had
made a little groove around the second finger. His ring — his
loved hand. With a sob he buried his face against the still
form, crying, "Rachel, my Rachel, my darling!"

The chimes, the carols of Christmas Eve were making the
winter twilight beautiful across the land. But no echo
reached *The Hermitage* where a solemn procession crossed
the garden to the spot where Rachel Jackson would rest.
Comforting words were spoken, then friends lingered on into
the evening with the grief-shattered man who was now
alone.

Turning to them, he said in a voice grown suddenly old,
"I can forgive all who have wronged me, but I will have to
pray fervently that I may have the grace to enable me to
forget or forgive any enemy who has ever maligned that
blessed one who is now safe from all suffering and sorrow,
whom they tried to shame for my sake."

The years ahead were full of tumult, of grave perplexities
and deep satisfactions for the gaunt, intrepid old warrior.
His administration which covered eight years was notable

for — among other things — the fact that the national debt was entirely paid off; that the Bank of the United States as the Government's official depository for public money was discontinued to make way for the present subtreasury system; and that two new states, Michigan and Arkansas, were admitted to the Union.

His foreign policy was so broad in vision that respect for American rights everywhere may be said to date from the Jackson administration. An epoch in American history was given his name. He had reached the peak. His work was done.

Martin Van Buren succeeded him, and on a March morning in 1837 the state carriage bearing the General, rolled out of the White House gates on the first lap of the journey back to the Hermitage for the years that remained. There, in the loved familiar surroundings, he had only to close his eyes a moment to see a heavy stockade gate swing slowly open. A dark-eyed girl in blue linsey-woolsey, her hair blowing in the wind, would stand there smiling.

"Come in," she would say, and as the gate swung wider he would recognize the voice as Rachel's.